TURNING OFF THE TAP:

Overcoming the
Real Reasons
We Overeat

Sara Best

DEDICATION

This book is dedicated to my grandmother, Dr. Joan Borland.

In 1984 my grandmother published a diet book called *Cast a Thin Shadow*, a book that "…encourages dieters to have fun, relax and enjoy their food while the pounds melt away!"

And while our approaches may differ, I know that she would have been utterly delighted to see my evolution of her ideas coming to the world in print.

I'm going to miss the excellent discussion we would have had about it all.

TABLE OF CONTENTS

Introduction

We all want to live long, healthy lives. We want to have lots of energy, lose some weight, feel fit and strong, and see that youthful glow when we look in the mirror. And we know that the way to get there is to eat better, move more and make time for self-care, right?

So, why don't we do it?

Isn't that the single most important question for us to answer? If we know what we want, and we know what we need to do to get there, why don't we do it?

"I don't know what to do."

"I don't have time to make healthy meals."

"It's a bad time right now, too much going on."

"I'm confused by all the conflicting diet advice out there."

"I love bread too much."

"It's too expensive."

"I'm addicted to sugar."

"I just love food. It makes me happy."

"I do really well all day but never have any willpower at night."

"My husband or kids are too picky. They won't eat the healthy stuff."

"It's easier to just order pizza."

These are just some of the hundreds of reasons clients, and people in my online community, have given me for why they haven't been able to stay on track with healthy eating. And I understand because I've said every single one of those things to myself at one time or another. But I would like to suggest that none of those are the real reason that we struggle to make healthy choices consistently.

I'm going to go out on a limb here and assume that picking up this book is not the first thing you've tried in your attempt to lose weight or find a way to stay on track with healthier eating, am I right? You've tried all the diets, all the programs and all the meal plans. You've bought the books and the DVDs. You've weighed, measured and tracked your food. You've avoided white foods and you've tried to eat the rainbow. You've tried to cut out carbs, fat, gluten and sugar. Heck, at one time or another, you've probably tried cutting out almost everything except oxygen.

And that's how most people are trying to lose weight or make changes to their health. They're spending countless hours focusing on what they should eat, how much, when and how often. They're wondering if they should be eating more protein and less carbs, or more fat and less sugar. They're looking for that perfect plan, recipe, shake or bar that will deliver the ideal nutritional profile combined with the maximum amount of metabolism-boosting super foods (while also tasting delicious and being super satisfying).

That's probably what you've been doing. I know it's what I was doing. Here's why that doesn't work – or why it works for a little while and then doesn't.

It doesn't work because it doesn't address a gigantic – probably the most crucial - piece of the puzzle. See, the truth is that just about any diet or healthy eating approach that appeals to you will work if - and here's the big if - if you stick with it consistently. If you go to the library or bookstore and choose any one of the thousands of healthy eating programs out there today, come home and implement all of it as directed, you will almost certainly lose weight and feel better.

But we don't do that, do we? We don't implement it. Or, we don't implement it consistently. And why not? We want to do better. And, despite our constant search for the answers, we actually already have a pretty solid understanding of what we should be eating and not eating (more fruits and veggies, less fast food, processed food and added sugar). So why don't we just do it?

To me, this is the only question that matters. Because, if you could just consistently do the things you know you need to do (make better food choices; move your body more; sleep better; take more time for self-care, etc.) then you'd already be most of the way to your goal. So, back to my original question: why don't we just do it?

We're smart. We're resourceful. We've done lots of other hard things in our lives. We've learned new things and overcome serious challenges. Why is this one so seemingly impossible?

You might think that it's because you lack the necessary willpower, or because you're too busy or lazy to plan, or because the people in your life sabotage you, or because you're addicted to carbs or sugar.

And there may be some truth to all of those things, but here's the real underlying answer: **We don't stick with it because we're trying to make changes that our brain simply will not accept because it's still hard-wired for our old ways.**

That's the missing piece of the puzzle. And, it's the reason that nothing you've tried so far has worked long-term. Everything you've tried so far has ignored this huge fact. Everything you've tried so far has told you to do things and make changes without changing the wiring in your brain first.

It's like trying to play a DVD in a VHS player. It's like trying to run new software on an old, incompatible operating system. It's never going to work. And the longer you try to do it, the more deeply you're going to feel like it's impossible. To illustrate this, I want you to paint a little picture for you...

Imagine you have out-of-town guests staying with you for the week. As a generous host you encourage them to make themselves at home during their visit. Your home is their home. You suggest that they especially make some time to enjoy a special treat - your recently renovated bathroom with the marble countertops, huge soaker tub and radiant heated floors! It took you two years to save for it, but it was worth every penny!

One day, you return home from running some errands and as you're taking off your jacket at the front door, a drop of water falls on you from the ceiling and you look down to see a puddle forming on the entryway floor. Confusion quickly turns to a pit in your stomach as you race up the stairs and turn the corner to the bathroom. There you find your bathroom door wide open, your guests on their hands and knees with what looks like every towel you own, sopping up more than an inch of water that's spreading over your expensive heated floors! They look panicked.

On the other side of the room you see that the enormous soaker tub is entirely filled and overflowing with water. The tap is still turned on full blast as more water cascades over the edges in a huge waterfall. The bathroom floor is an inch deep in water. It's spreading out onto the hardwood in the hall and running into the heating grates in the floor.

You look back at your guests, "What's going on?" you demand.

"The bathtub!!" they answer frantically. "We're trying to mop it up!! Do you have any more towels? Or do you have a different kind of towel – maybe ones that are thicker or more absorbent?"

You look down at them and back up at the tub, the tap still turned on full blast. You're so confused.

"Is the tap broken?" you ask over the din of the rushing water.

They look at you with blank looks on their faces. You point to the bathtub, "The tap. It's not working?"

"Oh, we didn't think of trying the tap," one of your guests says. "We're trying to deal with all this water!"

I tell this story because it illustrates what so many of us are doing when it comes to our efforts to stay on track with healthy eating. We're frantically trying to mop up the water, searching for more towels, bigger towels, more absorbent towels, instead of first turning off the tap!

This is what we're doing when we're constantly hunting for quicker, healthier recipes; or the right diet; or the latest low-carb protein bar. Yes, just like towels are going to be necessary if your bathtub overflows, recipes and information about nutrition are going to be important tools for you if you're trying to lose weight or get healthier, but unless you turn off the tap first, they are never going to solve the real problem.

And what's the tap when it comes to your food choices? It's that old operating system in your brain. That old operating system that still associates food with happiness and love; that turns immediately to food when you're tired, stressed or bored; that immediately feels the urge to overeat when you're at a restaurant or a party; and that feels most comfortable and happy when it gets to have it's favorite "comfort foods."

When we put all our energy into trying to implement new food choices without first updating that old operating system in our brain, it's like trying to deal with an overflowing bathtub by searching for the right towels instead of first turning off the tap!

It's exhausting because it constantly feels like an uphill battle and never works for longer than a day or a few days. And the longer you try to do it, the longer you're going to feel like you're failing.

I titled this book, *Turning Off the Tap: Overcoming the Real Reasons We Overeat* because what we must do instead is turn our attention first to turning off the tap, to updating that old operating system so that it stops fighting us at every turn and starts to welcome the healthy changes and embrace the new habits we want to create.

How do we do that? We do that by changing our approach. We do that by approaching the changes we want to make in a way that works with our brain's natural wiring, rather than against it and by actually reprogramming the parts of our old operating system that are holding us prisoner and keeping us stuck.

The truth is that our issues around food actually have very little to do with the food itself. You already know what you should be eating more of and what you should be eating less of. The problem isn't knowing what to eat, the problem is doing it! And this is why focusing on diets or carbs never sticks long-term. We must go below the surface and reprogram that old operating system if we want to create real, lasting change. That's what we need to be focusing on first.

Because, what you'll find is that, when you start by doing the work to reprogram and rewire the old habits and patterns your brain has around food, well, then you've literally changed your operating system. You've turned off the tap. And it starts to become so much easier to make the choices you need to make to get the results you want. That healthy lifestyle becomes your new automatic default. It becomes your new normal. You have literally become a new you!

It's time to stop playing on the surface. It's time to stop focusing on bread and ice cream and wine. It's time to stop blaming time and family and it's definitely time to stop assuming it's because of a weakness or character flaw on your part.

Together we're going to go deep, get real and wrestle this thing to the ground once and for all. Are you ready? Take my hand; we're going to do this together.

My Story

I remember sitting there on my couch in my yoga pants and sweatshirt, watching *The Real Housewives of Beverly Hills* with my hand deep in a bowl of potato chips (and a fair amount of chocolate covered almonds) and tears streaming down my face.

My husband and kids were fast asleep upstairs and here I was again – up way later than I should have been – in front of the TV, bingeing on junk food that I knew was making me fatter and sicker. A big part of me didn't even want it, but I honestly felt like I couldn't stop.

I felt powerless. I felt weak. I felt pathetic, trapped and terrified that I'd never be able to break this cycle and really make the changes that I knew I needed to make if I wanted to look and feel the way I wanted to look and feel.

I'd struggled with emotional eating for much of my life, but the problem got much worse after my second child was born. In his 18 months of life, he had only slept through the night on maybe a handful of occasions. That had been bearable when I was home on maternity leave because I could nap when he napped, but once I went back to work, it was torture. I quickly found myself in the middle of a perfect storm of stress, sleep deprivation and overwhelm.

My job at that time wasn't a check-your-brain at the door kind of job. I served as press secretary to a prominent and ambitious local politician. The hours were long, the pressure was high, and it was expected that I would be accessible by Blackberry at all times. Add to all of that the fact that my husband, who is an amazing and very hands-on dad, had recently left his steady job as an insurance broker to go to law school (a dream he'd always had). I was one hundred percent behind the decision, but it also meant that he was basically living at the library to study, leaving me on my own a lot to juggle two kids under the age of four on no sleep with my Blackberry buzzing constantly.

Food became my therapy. Once the crazy day was over and my husband and kids were all in bed, that was "my time." Time to hit the couch, turn on my favourite show and fix myself a bowl of salty and sweet treats. "I deserve this," I would tell myself. Fantasizing about those hours that I'd have for myself at night, and what I'd eat once I was alone, was often the only thing that kept me going during the day.

After almost a year of no sleep, stress that never let up, and a junk food diet, I felt like something in my brain broke and I had my first introduction to the world of depression. I didn't want to get out of bed. I would flip from yelling at my poor kids, to bursting into tears for no reason, to feeling completely numb to any feeling whatsoever.

As a result of all of it, I ended up gaining over 20 pounds and my doctor was becoming concerned that I was dangerously close to being pre-diabetic. I felt awful. I was exhausted all the time and I couldn't even stand to look at my body in the mirror.

My solution to all of this? Well, like so many of the women that I work with today, I focused much of my energy on beating myself up about it. Why couldn't I get my act together? I watched all these other working moms who seemed to be keeping all the balls in the air. They had great careers, awesome kids, ate perfectly and worked out daily (at least, that's what it looked like to me).

I remember reading a post that someone put on Facebook that said, "You and Beyoncé both have the same 24 hours in a day!" If Beyoncé could do it, what the hell was my problem? Why couldn't I be as determined and committed as Beyoncé? (um…FYI, Beyoncé also has a staff of nannies, chefs, house keepers and personal trainers)

I didn't want to live this way any more. I didn't want to weigh this much and feel this bad. I was determined to turn things around. So, I did what most people do. I tried every diet. Over the course of the next year I joined Weight Watchers, did South Beach, Atkins, and tried a macrobiotic diet. They all worked…for a bit, until my crazy life pushed me over again and I would say, "Screw it!" and end up back on that couch with my arm deep into a bag of chips with a chocolate bar chaser.

I wanted to change so badly, but I felt like a slave to the food. I didn't want to be eating it, but I honestly felt like I couldn't stop. I felt like I was trapped in a prison and I was utterly terrified that it was a life sentence.

I assumed that the reason I couldn't stay on track was that I just hadn't yet found the right approach, the right list of foods to eat and foods to avoid, the right recipes that would leave me satisfied, craving-free and a whole lot thinner. I became obsessed with idea that, if I could just figure out the right diet, the right carb to protein ratio, the right metabolism-boosting foods and just get a collection of the right healthy recipes, then I'd finally be able to overcome the cravings, stay on track, lose the weight and get my blood sugar under control.

This idea consumed me so deeply that I eventually decided to go back to school at night to become a Nutritionist. Surely as a Nutritionist I would know *exactly* what I should be eating and how much and then my battle with food would finally be over. I'd finally be in control. I'd be free.

So, off I went and after three years, I graduated as a Registered Holistic Nutritionist. I now had letters after my name that proved that I knew exactly what I should be eating to lose the weight and stay healthy. I knew that now my battle with food would be over and I couldn't wait for my new thinner and in-control self to start emerging. How exciting!

Except that nothing changed.

I'll never forget one night, just a couple of months after my graduation, when I found myself alone at home after a particularly crazy day at work. I could see my crisp new diploma hanging on the wall, but it didn't matter because there I was, right back on that couch, stuffing all that junk in my face. I felt nauseous, but I still couldn't stop eating.

I cried so hard that night because it felt like I was finally out of options. If I could be a Nutritionist who knew *exactly* what I should and shouldn't be eating and how much, and I *still* couldn't stop doing this, then clearly it was hopeless. I'd never be free. I'd always be fat and sick. And it was only going to get worse from here.

Tears poured down my face and I remember thinking that there must be something I was missing. How could I be a smart person who navigated a challenging and demanding job, have all the information I needed in my head about what to eat, and *still* be making the wrong choices all the time?

A lightbulb went off for me that night. Maybe it *wasn't* about the food at all. Maybe there was something else going on. Some other piece of the puzzle I was missing that would fit between my sincere desire to do better, and the unhealthy choices I always ended up making.

Around the same time, I'd joined a local yoga studio and, even though I was a total beginner to the practice, I had noticed that, on the days that I went to yoga, I seemed to have more control around food – even later into the day. What was going on there? Moreover, as part of my new yoga practice, I'd started meditating. I wasn't doing it every day, and I wasn't even sure that I was doing it right, but I was giving it a go, and I'd noticed that – like yoga – on the days that I meditated, I did feel less frazzled and less like I needed that "treat" at the end of the day to get me through. I couldn't put it all together yet, but there was something there – I just knew it!

I kept following the breadcrumbs, learning everything I could about food psychology and how the brain works when it comes to cravings, willpower and habits. I traveled to exotic locations on yoga and spiritual retreats, absorbing the principles of mindfulness and meditation. And I used all of those tools to dramatically transform, not only my relationship with food, but my life as a whole.

As a Nutritionist, I was still passionate about healthy food but, for the most part, I shifted my focus away from the food itself, and instead onto how and why my brain was experiencing the cravings and making the choices it was making around food. I learned how to feel my feelings rather than automatically trying to numb them with food. I began to literally rewire and reprogram the way my brain thought about and responded to food.

And that's when everything changed for me.

I finally had control over what I ate even when I'd had a crazy day at work or the kids were particularly challenging. From there I was able to lose the weight (and keep it off) and quit my stressful job and now I get the pleasure of teaching the same principles I learned to others all around the world.

I'm absolutely thrilled that you've decided to take this leap with me and explore a very different way of approaching this whole healthy eating and weight loss thing! I can't wait to share with you the missing puzzle pieces that I discovered and I'm so excited to see what lies ahead for you once you put those pieces in place!

Please remember that this is not about "fixing" you; you're already perfect. This is about giving you new insights and tools to help you change your relationship with food. And, more importantly, this is about helping you see your wholeness, tap into your greatness and awaken to the truth of who you are and what you're capable of.

I'm truly honoured to be joining you on this part of your path.

11

Your Declaration

Before we dive in, I want to invite you to make a declaration right now.

I know that you've tried a million things including diets, workouts, meal plans and shakes and I know that there's a little part of you that believes that, just like all of those, this probably isn't going to work either – be honest.

But here's the thing: your thoughts have the power to create your reality. And what you believe is very often what you receive.

It was Henry Ford who famously said, "Whether you think you can or you can't, you're right."

So, before you begin this new leg of your journey, I want you to shut down those old, negative thought habits (yes, they're habits), and I want you to stand up, stand tall and declare to the universe that this is the beginning of something very new for you.

First, I want you to read this declaration out loud and then I want you to open a journal or find a piece of paper and copy it out, word for word, in your own handwriting:

I am open to thinking about things in a way that I haven't before.

I am willing to be wrong about things I've believed to be true about myself and my relationship with food up to this point.

I am committed to being more deliberate with my thoughts and my actions.

I am ready to step into the highest version of myself.

I promise to embark on this work with honesty, bravery, patience and compassion for myself at all times.

Signed _____   Date _____

PART ONE:

Why What We've Been Trying So Far Hasn't Worked

You've tried everything to lose weight and create this balanced healthy lifestyle that you've heard so much about and that sounds really good to you. Some of those things worked for a while…until they didn't and you chalked it up to your own lack of willpower, skill, time or commitment.

I often ask the women in my online community to tell me about some of the craziest things they've done in their attempt to lose weight and the answers I get always astound me: grapefruit diets, cabbage soup, apple peels, laxatives, sweat suits, all white food, no white food, no carbs, no fat, no sugar, no gluten, coffee enemas, diet shakes, amphetamines, herbal supplements, starvation diets, exercise addiction, and that's just the beginning!

One woman even told a story about how she used to soak cotton balls in orange Tang and swallow them so she'd feel full but not take in any calories. WTF?!?!

These never sound to me like people who lack commitment or willpower. They sound to me like people who have been willing to do absolutely *anything*, no matter how painful or exhausting, to be free and create a better life for themselves. And this isn't something we've just tried for a week or two. Most of us have been trying different diets, shakes, bars, workouts, etc. for decades! Make no mistake, dieters are among the most committed people on the planet.

So, why, despite wanting it so badly and being willing to do almost anything to get it, have we continued to fail over and over and over again? Well, because we've been focused on the wrong thing and that's what we're going to explore in this first part of the book – the real reason why what we've been trying so far hasn't worked.

Spoiler alert: it has absolutely nothing to do with not enough time, a lack of willpower or a love of carbs.

Chapter 1

Your Big, Beautiful Brain

The place we need to start as we begin our journey into overcoming the real reasons we overeat is the brain. The human brain is incredible and we're still only at the tip of the iceberg in terms of what we fully understand about its inner workings. I am not a neuroscientist nor in any way qualified to attempt to explain everything that your brain does or how it works. However, since your brain is where every single one of your food choices is being made, and since it so often feels like there's a tug of war going on up there between what we *know* we should be doing and what we *actually* end up doing, it's important that we spend some time here trying to understand it all a bit better.

Also, what I see so often is women beating themselves up for not being strong, committed or organized enough to reach their goals, and I need you to know that your frustrating habits and patterns around food have very little to do with your strength of character, and a whole lot to do with the neurochemistry and neurocircuitry going on up in your brain.

For our purposes here (and because I'm not a neuroscientist), I'm going to grossly simplify things and introduce you to just two key parts of your big, beautiful brain: your **limbic brain** and your **prefrontal cortex**. These two parts of your brain are the ones battling it out every day over whether you're going to go to the gym after work or lie on the couch, or order the nachos or the salad so it's important that we get to know them better.

Limbic Brain

On the timeline of human evolution, your limbic brain is the part of your brain that's been around the longest. Because of this, you'll often see it referred to as the "lizard brain," "reptilian brain," or "caveman brain." This part sits deep in the centre of your brain and it's responsible for the functions of your most basic survival. Your limbic brain controls things like your breathing, heart rate, body temperature and your "fight or flight" response. This part of your brain has existed in humans for hundreds of thousands of years. It doesn't care about how you look in skinny jeans, or if you have back fat. It only cares about your immediate survival.

Prefrontal Cortex

Your prefrontal cortex on the other hand is the more modern part of your brain. This is the large part of your brain that sits up front, right behind your forehead. Your prefrontal cortex is much newer to the game on the evolutionary timeline. This part of your brain deals with logic, rational thought and weighing pros and cons. It cares about things like getting to work on time, which car to buy and making long-term plans.

So, given that the limbic brain controls things like survival and the prefrontal cortex controls things like new car purchases, which do you think carries more weight? Which do you think wins when they go head-to-head against one another in a fight? That's right, the caveman almost always wins.

If you think about it, this make a lot of sense. Obviously, we want things like keeping our heart beating and maintaining our body core temperature to be at the top of the list when our brain is prioritizing tasks. However, this hierarchy isn't so helpful when you consider the fact that the limbic brain is also where habits like night-time snacking reside, and the prefrontal cortex is where you make rational decisions like, "I don't want to snack at night anymore."

If you have a habit of heading to the kitchen for potato chips at night, that habit lives inside your limbic brain. If you decide that you want to lose weight and sleep better you might try to engage your very rational prefrontal cortex to come out and attempt to break that old night-time snacking habit. Now you've pitted the limbic brain against the prefrontal cortex and this isn't going to end well for you (remember what I said a moment ago about how the caveman almost always wins?).

Imagine that the limbic brain is a skittish honey-badger and the pre-frontal cortex is a wise old college professor. Certainly, with the right approach, plan and tools, the professor is entirely capable of controlling the honey-badger, but if you just throw a freaked-out honey-badger into a pen to battle an unsuspecting college professor, my money's on the honey-badger every time. And that's what's going on most of the time when we attempt to break old ingrained habits around food - our limbic brain and our pre-frontal cortex get pitted against one another, and guess which one wins?

The fact is that, despite all our modern advances in technology, insights into the universe, and plethora of smartphone apps, when you take a closer look at what's actually driving most of your thoughts, reactions and choices every day it's still basically caveman software. Or, if you prefer, you have a scared honey-badger running most of your life.

Now, that's not to say that the prefrontal cortex can't over-ride the limbic brain – it can. That's how you can stay and give the speech even when you want to bolt out the stage door, or how you can smile at your co-worker and ask about her weekend even when you want to punch her in the face. We use our prefrontal cortex to over-ride our limbic brain all the time, but it requires the right approach, plan and tools, all of which we're going to be talking about here as we go on.

But first, given the fact that your caveman brain is really running the show a lot of the time, and given that it's always prudent to attempt to understand your adversary as best as you possibly can before battle, I think we should get to know it a bit better before we move on.

The Mission Statement

Most big companies and organizations have what's called a "mission statement." Your family might even have one. A mission statement is a short declaration – a few sentences at most – that sums up what the single driving aim or focus of the organization is. Its purpose is to give everyone in that organization clarity around what their collective main objective should be so that, if they ever have a question about what to do, they can answer it by considering which option most closely aligns with the mission statement.

For example, the mission statement at LinkedIn is, "To connect the world's professionals to make them more productive and successful."

The BBC: "To enrich people's lives with programmes and services that inform, educate and entertain."

Google: "To organize the world's information and make it universally accessible and useful."

Your caveman brain has a mission statement too. Remember that, even though we live in the modern world, your brain is still largely wired in the exact same way that it was hundreds of thousands of years ago. This means that, just as it was for our Neanderthal ancestors, your caveman brain is hard-wired with one, singular mission statement: **avoid pain, seek pleasure and expend as little energy as possible to do so.**

And it's important to note before we go on that "pain" is not just physical pain, but is associated with anything that your brain believes threatens your safety and survival, and that "pleasure" is not just things that are fun but rather refers to anything that your brain views as promoting your safety and survival.

The goal back in caveman days was to use this programmed mission statement to keep you alive long enough to mate and pass on your genetic material so that the species could continue. It's basic biology and all living things approach life with the same mission statement. The monkey feels hungry and eats the lowest hanging fruit on the tree. The bean plant grows away from the shade and towards the sun in a straight line. The racoon avoids the cold of winter by moving into your already built and toasty attic.

No matter what plans you've made or what goals you've identified with the more modern, rational part of your brain, that old caveman software is going to fight you any time to try to deviate too far from this mission statement.

Now, a hundred thousand years ago, pain looked like things that could kill you: famine, freezing temperatures, contaminated food, big animals that wanted to eat you or other tribes that wanted to fight you and take your stuff. Today, pain may look at little different. In our modern world, we rarely find ourselves starving or freezing or running away from tigers or warring tribes. Today, the things that our brains typically register as pain usually look more like feelings; feelings of exhaustion, overwhelm, worry and stress. When your brain senses these it identifies them as pain and it immediately locks you onto what it perceives to be the most efficient path away from that pain and towards pleasure.

Remember that "pleasure" refers to those things that your brain associates with promoting your safety and security including calorie-dense foods, social connection and accumulation of resources. What that translates into in our modern world is that, for some people pleasure can come in the form of shopping, drinking, gambling, drugs, romantic relationships or social media, but, if you're reading this, I'm guessing that, for you, it's very often food. And not steamed kale, but some form of sugar or highly refined carbohydrates. I'm talking about chips, ice cream, chocolate, pretzels, chocolate covered pretzels, etc.

The Problem with Dieting

Want to know another thing that your brain registers as pain? Deprivation (a.k.a. dieting). When your brain senses that it might be deprived of the things that make it feel safe and secure, it's mission statement programming immediately kicks in and it gets locked back onto that pleasure-seeking trajectory. We've all experienced this, you tell your brain that it can't have sugar, and guess what it immediately it decides it wants more than anything

23

else in the world?

There are many reasons why dieting doesn't work, but the fact that it goes against your brain's natural wiring is certainly one of them.

Familiar = Safe

It's also important to understand that, in addition to your caveman brain registering feelings like stress, boredom and sadness as pain, it also identifies things that are *unfamiliar* in the same way.

To your caveman brain, familiar equals safe and unfamiliar equals danger. We repeat old habits and patterns again and again, even when they hurt us, because, at a deeper level, they're familiar and to your caveman brain that equals safety.

This is one of the reasons why, when you find yourself exhausted at the end of a long day you decide to dig out those sweet or salty snacks and pour yourself a glass of wine. You know that doing some journaling and heading to bed early would be a healthier choice that would make you feel better and move you closer to your goals of losing weight and not feeling tired all the time, but you don't do it (at least not most of the time).

The chips, sweets or wine feel both wonderfully familiar, and like the fastest and most efficient way out of the discomfort we're feeling from being stressed or tired or bored. Your caveman brain locks onto them and won't let go, leaving you feeling like you have zero control.

When you do try to stop your caveman brain from doing what's familiar and avoiding the pain you're feeling by seeking the pleasure of food, you almost always lose. And this is because you're trying to work against our brain's mission statement. You're trying to wrestle your brain into doing something it's not programmed to do. And, since that's a David and Goliath (or a panicked honey-badger and unprepared college professor)-style battle, you're mostly losing.

To make matters worse, what we typically do when we find ourselves falling again and again into these unhealthy but familiar behaviors is we beat ourselves up. "Why can't I say no?" "Why can't I stay on track?" "Why am I always so weak?" "Why can't I do what other people do?" At some level we imagine that by reprimanding ourselves and making ourselves feel awful about what we've eaten, we'll stop the behavior.

However, this actually has the exact *opposite* effect because your brain registers that nasty internal judgement as more pain and immediately sends you searching for more pleasure to get away from it. This means one more bowl of ice cream or another handful (or five) of those chocolate-covered-pretzels.

So, what should we be doing instead? How do we calm the terrified honey-badger of our limbic system so that the wise college professor known as the pre-frontal cortex can make a better decision? What we should be doing is thinking about how we can work *with* our brain's natural wiring to get what we want instead of against it. If you can't beat 'em, join 'em!

Replace Judgement with Curiosity

Since we now understand that your brain is hard-wired to avoid pain and seek pleasure, it makes sense that, when trying to adapt new habits, you'd want to work on avoiding pain as much as possible in order to avoid triggering that reward-seeking, self-sabotaging behavior.

Now, you have little control over the external factors that cause you pain (although you have a great deal of control over how you let those factors affect you – more on that later), but you can certainly start minimizing the amount of extra pain you are inflicting on yourself with all that self-judgement. This is where I like to share with my students one of my favorite mantras. When you're craving foods that don't serve you, or when you've made a choice you're not thrilled with, instead of immediately judging yourself and beating yourself up (pain), stop, take a breath and replace that judgement with *curiosity*.

It works like this: You're desperately craving something that you know isn't good for you, or you just finished eating way too much of something that you wish you hadn't. Notice the judgement that immediately leaps up and make the conscious choice to put that judgement aside for a few moments. Take that time to view the situation through a different lens. Not the old lens of self-judgement and "Why did I do that?" but a new, objective lens of "Hmmm, well that's interesting."

In Buddhist teachings they talk of the "**second arrow**." The first arrow is the one that the world shoots at you and the way that you react to it. This is the hurt, the stress, the fear, the worry that you're feeling as a result of outside forces. But the second arrow is the one you shoot at yourself when you blame yourself and beat yourself up for the first arrow. You don't have a lot of control over the first arrow, but you do get to choose whether or not you shoot that second arrow.

Get curious. Think of yourself as a scientist and ask yourself some probing questions. How are you feeling right now? Are you truly physically hungry or are you wanting this food for some purpose other than fuel? What's going on in your life, your environment, your body and your mind right now that's making it feel like you must have this food? What are you hoping this food will do for you?

You might love the taste of ice cream, but my guess is that you also love the taste of peaches or blueberries or watermelon but you're not mindlessly bingeing on those in front of the TV. Your brain is looking for something in that ice cream (beyond just the taste) and the first step in rewiring that relationship is to understand what that something is.

It's not a character weakness to crave ice cream every night. There's a real reason that it's happening and you just need to get curious and start following the breadcrumbs back to start uncovering what that reason is. Reframing the picture in this way will help remove the added pain of the self-criticism and guilt and thereby reduce your brain's natural tendency to seek out more pleasure by eating even more.

Working *With* Your Brain's Mission Statement

We've looked at how we can avoid having our own guilt and self-judgement about a not-so-great choice drive us to make even more poor choices. But, how do we start working with our brain's natural wiring – its mission statement – to avoid making the unhealthy choices in the first place?

First, make the healthy choices *pleasurable*. We want to do everything we can to turn the healthier choices we want to be making into something your brain perceives as *pleasure* rather than deprivation (a.k.a. pain). In order to do this we need to have a clearer understanding of *why* we want to lose the weight, have more energy, live longer, etc. This is part of the reason that I'm always asking my students to spend some time thinking about the big, beautiful vision they have for their health and their lives. We're going to dive deep into exactly how you create that kind of a compelling vision and how you connect with it as a daily practice later, but for now, you can start asking yourself some simple questions:

- Why do I want to eat better, move more, lose the weight and live a long and healthy life?
- What do I struggle to do now that would feel much easier if I reached my goals?
- Who would I be able to love longer and spend more time with?
- How would my daily life change?
- Who would I inspire?
- What words would other people use to describe me?

Take some time to think about these questions and get super specific about the answers. You should be able to see this future life of yours like an incredible movie in your head. Again, much more on this in Part Two.

Once you have *that* amazing movie playing in your head, that will start to feel like pleasure to your brain and, because your brain is hard-wired to avoid pain and seek pleasure, you will slowly begin to feel yourself being naturally drawn to the choices and behaviors

27

that align with it and move you closer to it. No more tug of war! No more fighting your own brain!

Second, make the healthy choices *easy*. Remember the last part of the mission statement that your brain is living by: avoid pain, seek pleasure and *expend as little energy as possible to do so*. In addition to avoiding pain and seeking pleasure, your brain is also wired to use as little energy as possible in the process. If your brain had a motto to accompany its mission statement, it would be: "Always take the path of least resistance!" If the elephant has the choice between some tasty bushes that are five miles to the left, or some tasty grass that's a hundred feet to the right, you better believe it's turning right.

Your brain works the same way the elephant's. If your brain is feeling pain (exhaustion, stress, worry) and it sees the choice to be between going for a walk and going to bed early on the left (which you know is the healthier choice), and a bowl of ice cream and the couch to the right, you better believe it's turning right – just like that elephant. The pleasure of the ice cream and the couch is much closer and more immediate. That's part of the reason why it wins. We prefer instant gratification.

Psychologists call this, "delay discounting." It means that any reward (pleasure) becomes less appealing to your brain the further away it is – either in time or space. This is why we need to start doing everything we can to make the unhealthy choices feel less available. You're going to learn some really specific tools to help you do that as we go on.

Happy Binges

Okay, so hopefully this all makes sense about why we turn to food when we're feeling uncomfortable. But what about when we're happy? Why do we also find ourselves giving in to temptation and going overboard when we're feeling happy like when we're on vacation, at a party, or out at a restaurant with friends? We're already feeling pleasure then, why do our brains feel so pulled to the junk food at those times?

Well, this requires us to dig a little deeper into how your brain defines "pleasure." You might think of pleasure as a week in Jamaica with your family, or Saturday night at the karaoke bar with your friends, but in your brain's language, when we refer to "pleasure" what we're really talking about is *safety*. What your brain is looking for when it's seeking out "pleasure" is a feeling of *familiarity*.

What you're usually feeling when you're out at a party or on vacation, is excitement. We're enjoying ourselves, yes, but in our brain's language excitement feels unfamiliar, stressful and potentially dangerous. For this reason, excitement (even when it's fun) often drives us to eat to cope with these feelings.

Okay, we've spent quite a bit of time examining the primary part of your caveman brain's mission statement, "Avoid pain and seek pleasure." Next, we're going to dig even deeper into one of the key ways that your brain fulfills the second part of its mission statement, "...and expend as little energy as possible to do so." You're going to see why this seemingly harmless intention is actually one of the biggest reasons you've struggled with food for so long.

TURNING OFF THE TAP

Chapter 2

Neurons that Fire Together, Wire Together

In the last chapter we talked about your caveman brain's mission statement: avoid pain, seek pleasure and expend as little energy as possible to do so. The reason that your caveman brain is always seeking to conserve energy wherever it can is not because it's lazy, rather it's thinking ahead. It's aiming to preserve as much energy as it can at all times just in case you need to suddenly run away from a tiger!

You might assume that the parts of your body that eat up the most energy are your limbs and muscles – maybe even your heart. But pound for pound, the organ that actually burns through the most calories in a day is your brain. Your brain isn't that large; it accounts for only 2 per cent the average person's total body weight, but it burns through 20 per cent of our daily energy output!

Thinking burns a lot of calories. And one of the things that expends the most energy in your brain is learning something new. Think about when you first learned how to tie your shoes or play an instrument or learn a new language. It took a ton of mental energy and you could only work on it for a little while before you probably needed to take a break.

Now imagine if you had to re-learn how to tie your shoes, brush your teeth and walk every morning. Your brain wouldn't have any energy left to run away from, or make a plan to escape, any possible danger. Spending all that energy or re-learning daily tasks would leave you vulnerable to harm or even death by tiger!

Because of this, your brain has developed an excellent strategy to help you conserve a whole lot of that energy and it involves **automating** as much of your life and your daily tasks as possible.

Conscious Mind vs. Automatic Mind

When it comes to completing tasks, your brain is divided into two areas – the conscious mind and automatic mind. Both are very different, but both are also very important.

The **conscious mind** is the part that you use to take in new information coming in through your senses, assess its relevance and meaning for you and your life at that moment and takes action (if required) based on that assessment.

The conscious mind is at work, for example, when you're driving through a new city. You're looking at signs, listening to the GPS tell you where to go, and making new decisions based on that information second by second. You're very present and very aware. You're also burning a lot of calories because, as we discussed, that much thinking requires an enormous amount of energy.

The **automatic mind** on the other hand is the part that handles all the decisions and activities that you've *already* assessed in the past. Once you've assessed the information and made a decision about it a few times, your brain quickly shuttles that task to the automatic mind so that it can take over the work and simply repeat what you decided to do before without the conscious mind having to check in again. The automatic mind is at work when you're brushing your teeth, tying your shoes or walking to work. Unlike your conscious mind, your automatic mind runs on very little energy. It's highly efficient.

In car terms, think of your conscious mind as the Hummer and your automatic mind as the Tesla!

Because your brain's mission statement requires it to conserve energy, it's always seeking to shuttle work from the energy-sucking conscious mind to the energy-efficient automatic mind. This means that as soon as you repeat something – an action or a thought – a few times, your brain works quickly to move that action or thought into the automatic mind so that you can continue to repeat it over and over again without having to give it almost any thought.

This is of course very helpful when it comes to things like walking, not so helpful when it comes to eating tubs of popcorn at the movies or bingeing at night on the couch in front of the TV.

So, the obvious next question is, when we've automated a behavior that we don't want to be doing any more, how do we un-automate it? Well, to answer that, we must first understand how your automatic mind actually works and how it makes it so that you can walk and talk and brush your teeth without thinking about it anymore.

Neural Pathways

In 1949, a Canadian neuropsychologist named Donald Hebb distilled the complicated mechanics of the automatic brain into one powerful sentence: **"Neurons that fire together, wire together."**

What this means is that when our brain cells communicate with one another to make us perform a task, one brain cell releases a chemical (a neurotransmitter) that the other brain cell absorbs. When we repeat a thought or an action over and over, and that neurotransmitter moves between those brain cells again and again, the connection between them strengthens. The more we repeat that action or have that thought, the faster that neurotransmitter starts to be passed from brain cell to brain cell.

Eventually, the process happens so rapidly, that an actual *physical* connection between those cells is created. Neurons that fire together, wire together. This wiring, or connection, between them that is formed is called a **"neural pathway."** These neural pathways allow thoughts and actions that we repeat over and over again to become automatic. This is the basis of the automatic brain.

It's why we practice things like swinging a golf club properly or playing a piece of music on the piano over and over again. Because we know that, with enough practice, the movement will eventually become automatic and we'll be able to do it without even thinking about it.

You've likely heard the term, "muscle memory" and that's just another way of describing this notion that neurons that fire together, wire together. It's not your muscles that are remembering – it's the development of new neural pathways in your brain resulting from repetition that eventually allow you to do the action automatically, without even thinking about it with your conscious mind.

Have you ever been brushing your teeth while thinking about an email that you need to return when you get to work? Or have you ever driven to the grocery store, arrived and realized that your mind was somewhere else entirely and you barely even remember the drive there? Those are neural pathways at work!

Here's an analogy for this that I like to use: Imagine you were a kid again and you had to walk through a big, grassy field to get to school every day. The first time you made the trek through the field it would be hard to get through. You'd have to really focus on whacking down all that long grass and regularly peering over the tall plants and weeds to make sure you were walking in the right direction towards school.

However, after a week or two of doing this again and again, a path would form along the route you'd been taking. You wouldn't have to work hard to whack that grass down anymore, or pay attention to what direction you were walking in. You'd be able to just follow the path that you'd created through the grass and you'd soon start to do the walk automatically, without even thinking about it. You could be thinking about your weekend plans and you'd suddenly find yourself in the schoolyard because you would have simply followed the path you'd made.

That path through the grassy field is just like a neural pathway in your brain. Once it's formed through enough repetition, your brain just follows it and no longer needs to think about what it's doing any more. It becomes automatic. However, it also means that doing anything different feels hard and awkward and even exhausting.

The same principle is at work with our habits around food. Just as your brain creates neural pathways around activities you've repeated like tying your shoes and walking, it's also created neural pathways around the behaviors you've repeated with food.

This network of neural pathways that form the automatic mind, is the basis of the state that we often refer to as "auto-pilot." And as helpful as auto-pilot is when you're brushing your teeth or tying your shoes, it becomes your number one enemy when you're trying to break old habits and create a new, healthier relationship with food.

This is because the automatic mind is often one of the reasons why we eat when we're not hungry (we always eat at this time, or with these people, or in this place), or why we have a cup of coffee in the car or reach for sweets after a meal.

And why we associate certain situations with certain behaviours (e.g., eating popcorn at the movies, ordering the same potato skins at the local bar after work, snacking in front of the TV, etc.). And why we gravitate to food when we have certain feelings such as stress, anxiety, boredom or loneliness.

At one point we did these things consciously but then we repeated them over and over again so our brains went to work building neural pathways to automate the behaviors for us so we wouldn't have to use our conscious mind to think about them anymore. Eventually, thanks to those neural pathways, we started to do them without even thinking about them and now, to do anything else, feels uncomfortable, challenging and unsatisfying.

And, remember earlier when we talked about how your brain associates things that are familiar with safety, and things that are unfamiliar with potential danger to be avoided at all costs? Well, all those neural pathways that your brain has now created around your unhealthy food habits also make those habits feel...you guessed it – familiar! So, combine a habit reinforced by strong neural pathways, with the accompanying feeling of familiarity and safety around that habit and you have the recipe for a behavior that your caveman brain is going to hold onto at all costs and that, as a result, feels almost impossible to break.

To make matters worse, in addition to lots of unhealthy habits around food that your brain has automated, there's something else that your brain has created deep neural pathways around that is now stopping you from creating the balanced, healthy relationship with food that you long for. This is something that the diet industry has taught you and encouraged you to practice and practice and now, thanks to your automatic mind, you do it automatically. What I'm talking about is ignoring and disregarding the signals that your body is telling you about what it truly needs to eat, how much and when.

The dieting model trains you to disconnect from your body. It says, if you're hungry, ignore it. If you're craving something, ignore it. Think this diet shake is disgusting? Drink it anyway.

You practiced this approach for years and years, and guess what? That's right, your brain formed neural pathways around that behavior and it eventually became automatic. In fact, it's so ingrained in you at this point that even now, when you've come to see that this approach hasn't worked and you want to reconnect with your body and start to truly fuel and nourish it properly, you find it very difficult to hear and understand the signals that it's sending you about what it actually needs. You struggle to know when you're hungry, when you're satisfied, or when you've overeaten until you're uncomfortably full or even feeling sick. You no longer speak your body's language. The lines of communication between your brain and your body have corroded and shut down thanks to so many years of dieting. We're going to dive deeper into exactly what you can do to start to break those old neural pathways and re-open those lines of communication later on in Part Two.

Okay, so the bad news is that, right now, your old habits and patterns around a lot of not-so-healthy behaviors around food are being reinforced by deep neural pathways in your automatic brain. As a result, it feels hard, impossible even, to be consistent with healthier choices like avoiding refined sugar, not snacking at night, or prepping healthy meals on the weekend.

But, here's the good news: because your brain is a habit-making machine, it cannot help but form neural pathways around, and eventually automate, behaviors that you repeat again and again. Remember, neurons that fire together, wire together. They can't help themselves! So, we can use that to our advantage as a way to create new, healthier habits. We can force *different* neurons to fire together so that they eventually wire together. And it turns out that your brain is actually really good at doing this. It's not easy, and it feels hard at first, but it's entirely possible.

Neuroscientists call this beautiful ability that the brain has to abandon old neural pathways, and create new ones, **"neuroplasticity."** I love this term because it conveys the idea that, rather than being carved in stone, the neural pathways in your brain are somewhat plastic and therefore changeable. It means that, with the right approach, plan and tools, you can literally reprogram and rewire the way you brain thinks about food!

This also means that you can do away with the idea that you're going to need to have buckets of willpower for the rest of your life if you're going to stay on track with health eating. Or that you just have a "sweet tooth" and that you're never going to be able to change that. It means that the brain can actually be changed through our thoughts and behaviours because, every time we engage in and repeat a positive behaviour, we create new neural pathways and increase the likelihood that we'll do that again.

TURNING OFF THE TAP

Next, let's dive deeper into these habits that your brain is forming with these neural pathways. It turns out that every habit you have follows the same structure and that it's this specific structure that holds the key to breaking old ones and creating new ones.

Chapter 3

Habit Loops

The habits that are formed by your automatic brain with neural pathways work in loops. Every habit follows this same loop structure. It goes like this: you encounter a cue, that triggers a certain routine or behavior, which delivers a reward, which teaches you to notice and respond to that cue in the same way again the next time you encounter it.

Cue, behavior, reward; psychologists call this the "**Habit Loop.**"

The reason that habits are so frustrating and so hard to break is because, once that cue, routine, reward structure has been set up in your brain and you've repeated it enough times that neural pathways have been created to automate it, it's very difficult to break the loop. Every time you encounter that cue, you feel compelled to do the behavior to get the reward.

The **cues** for your not-so-healthy eating habits could include things like a certain feeling (stress, worry, boredom, fatigue, overwhelm, etc.), a time of day (Sunday mornings, afternoon slump, evening on the couch, etc.), specific people (family, friends, etc.), or certain activities (movies, driving, parties, watching TV, etc.).

The **behavior** is the thing you do or think when you experience that cue. For our purposes here, this is eating not-so-healthy foods, overeating or mindlessly eating.

And the **reward** is generally a positive feeling, feeling connected to friends or family, or simply some relief from the uncomfortable feeling that was your original cue.

So, a habit loop around food could look like feeling exhausted after a long day (cue), grabbing your favourite snacks and heading to the couch to watch TV (behavior), and feeling like you're treating yourself or taking care of yourself (reward).

Now, don't be misled by the term "reward." The reward part of your habit loop is not always something that we would consider positive. Very often the reward that your brain is looking for is simply a feeling that is *familiar*. Remember how we learned that your brain loves things that are familiar (even if they are also unpleasant) because, to your brain, familiarity equals safety and safety is what your brain wants more than anything else?

For example, as strange as it may sound, when I was still struggling with binge eating, one of my rewards was feeling nauseous. I know, weird, right? I would start out feeling tired and worn out from my day (that was my cue). Then I'd wait until evening when everyone else was in bed or in their rooms and I'd plop myself down on the couch in front of the TV and binge on chips and chocolate (that was my behavior). And my reward was first some sense of relief from those uncomfortable feelings because I felt like I was getting a treat and like I was filling my empty cup in some way. But it was also the wall of nausea I would eventually hit from my bingeing. That nauseous feeling was familiar to me so I kind of craved it.

I found it almost impossible to stop before I felt nauseous and would keep returning to the kitchen for just a few more chips, and just a few more squares of chocolate, until I literally felt sick. That's when I knew I'd had enough. Even though I didn't enjoy feeling nauseous it was still part of the reward for my habit loop because it was the signal my brain was looking for to know that I'd had enough. It was familiar which made it feel safe and, in some weird way, comfortable.

Thoughts are Habits Too

It's important to recognize that most of your thoughts are habits too, and they follow the same cue, behavior, reward loop only the behavior is a thought. You encounter a cue, which triggers a thought, which delivers a reward.

Most of the thoughts you'll have today are the exact same thoughts you had yesterday, and the day before, which is why you end up making the same choices and getting the same outcomes.

For example, you open the mailbox to see a bill (cue), that triggers a thought such as "we don't have enough money" (behavior), which feels comfortable and familiar because it makes you feel like you're preparing yourself for the worst (reward), which then ensures that every time you open the mailbox and see a bill you feel anxious and have the thought, "we don't have enough money."

We often have negative thought habit loops surrounding our relationship with food. These thought loops usually involve what I call, "**The Mean Voice**" in your head. For example, you look in the mirror while getting dressed in the morning (cue), you immediately start having thoughts about how overweight you are, how awful you look and how you're never going to get a handle on this (behavior), and then you either resolve to do better today (reward of hope) or you think, "Screw it, I might as well have the BLT for breakfast because what's the point?" (reward of freedom from the deprivation of dieting).

In many ways, we actually become *addicted* to our thought habit loops. We have a familiar thought (often negative), it creates a little stress response in the body with the release of hormones like adrenaline and cortisol, this triggers a little stimulation in the brain that we start to get used to so that, in the absence of any real stress, we'll actually subconsciously go *looking* for stressful or worrying thoughts in order to trigger that stress response and get that little stimulation in the brain that feels so familiar.

And, time for a little tough love here, it's important to recognize that giving up also becomes a habit. How often have you committed to eating better and exercising more, and then given up again shortly thereafter because the cravings were too strong or it all just felt too hard? As soon as you start doing it, breaking your old habits around food feels difficult, uncomfortable and overwhelming (cue). You start having thoughts like, "This isn't a good time to do this," or "It would be better to start this after that wedding we're going to this weekend," or "This is too hard for me to do right now," (behavior). And then you decide to go back to your old, familiar habits (reward).

As uncomfortable as it may be, if we want to break these old patterns that have been defining us and keeping us stuck for years, we need to be prepared to challenge the excuses we keep falling back on, recognize them as the thought habit loops that they are, and learn how to break them so that we can start focusing instead on thoughts that are more empowering and effective at helping us reach our goals.

So, we've talked a bit about how habits work and how habits determine, not only our actions, but our thoughts as well. The next obvious question is, how do we change them? How do we break old habit loops that are keeping us stuck in old patterns?

Breaking Habit Loops

Well, if we think about the three parts of our habit loop (cue, behavior, reward), the cue is often impossible to change. We can't change the fact that stressful things are going to happen, or that we're going to open the mailbox and find bills, or that we're going to find ourselves in social situations, or that evening time is going to roll around every day.

It's also very difficult to change the reward. As we've learned, your brain is hard-wired to avoid pain and seek pleasure, which means that it's always going to want some payoff for any activity or thought it does or has.

So, **the secret to changing any habit is to keep the cue and the reward and replace the *behavior*.** In order to do that, we must first *identify* each of those components in our own habits. Sometimes this is easier said than done.

The **behavior** is easy – that's the thing you do that you don't like (i.e., overeating at parties, eating junk food on the couch at night, eating when you're stressed, etc.)

The **cue** and **reward** can be tougher to identify, and this is because of what we learned earlier about how the automatic brain creates neural pathways around behaviors that we repeat over and over again, so that eventually we do them without even thinking.

Most of the unhealthy habits we have around food are things that we've been repeating for years, or decades, and those habit loops have now become deeply entrenched in our automatic brain, making it difficult for us to identify and label them.

Let's start by searching for the cue. Begin to notice what's happening, where you are, who you're with and what you're thinking and feeling immediately *before* you make the not-so-great food choice. Since we're doing most of this automatically now, you'll likely need to start by doing this in hindsight. So, when you find yourself making that not-so-healthy choice, stop as soon as you can, replace judgement with curiosity, and ask yourself, "What was I just doing, where was I, who was I with, what was I thinking and feeling right before I ate this, or right before this craving emerged?" If you do this consistently for a little while, you'll start to notice recurring themes and patterns. These are your cues.

It's important to understand that, while our cues feel like they are external to us, they are actually ultimately internal. Nothing external can make us feel anything. Things happen externally and then we choose to react to them with a certain thought and feeling. It's that thought and feeling that then become our cue to turn to food.

Next, let's try to identify the reward. Rewards are often related to cues, but not always. If your cue is an uncomfortable feeling like stress, anxiety or boredom, then the reward is often simply a brief sense of relief from that uncomfortable feeling. If your cue is a certain person such as your partner or a good friend or group of friends, the reward can be a deeper sense of closeness with them (e.g., this is our "thing" that we do together). If your cue is a time

43

of day (pastry with your coffee in the morning, or junk food on the couch at night) then the true cue is often not so much the actual time as it is a way that you typically feel at that time (e.g., exhausted and sluggish in the morning, overwhelmed and drained at night, stressed and tired at 3pm, etc.), so the reward is some relief from that feeling (e.g., the sugar and caffeine picks you up in the morning, the junk food makes you feel like you're having the treat you deserve at night, etc.).

A helpful question to ask yourself to help tease out the reward you're seeking is, "**How am I hoping this food will make me feel?**" Keep asking that question whenever you're craving something and, like with the cues, you'll start to see themes and patterns emerge in the type of rewards your brain is seeking.

It's also helpful to start to examine the positive, healthy habits you have right now to see what cues and rewards you have around those behaviors that are currently working for you. Those healthy habits can give you some great awareness about what cues and rewards your brain already responds to positively.

Once you've identified the cues and rewards that book-end the behaviors you want to change, the next step is to pick a different, healthier behavior that you can do when you encounter that cue, and that will deliver the same (or a similar) reward.

Too often we attempt to throw the baby out with the bathwater. We want to rid ourselves of an unhealthy behavior but in trying to simply stop doing the behavior, we end up inadvertently also denying our brain the reward it was seeking. This is a difficult uphill battle because, as we've learned, your brain is hard-wired to avoid pain and seek pleasure. When you try to deny your brain its reward, you are fighting its natural wiring and that's partly why it feels so hard and why we end up returning to our old behaviors again and again. It's not necessarily the behavior your brain wants, it's the reward. Thus, the key instead is not to simply stop the unhealthy behavior but rather to *replace* the unhealthy behavior with something else that still delivers the same or a similar reward.

For example, say your cue is the end of the day and feeling exhausted and utterly depleted, and the reward you seek is feeling relaxed and like you're getting a "treat" for surviving your crazy day. Instead of the routine of sitting on the couch, watching Netflix and eating potato chips, a different routine could be having a cup of herbal tea with a square of dark chocolate and doing a jigsaw puzzle in your pyjamas. Or, maybe lighting some candles and doing some gentle stretching before heading to bed a little earlier.

In the final part of this book we're going to dive deeper into the world of self-care. The tools that you learn there will be very helpful as you do this work to replace your old unhealthy habit loop behaviors with new, healthier ones.

In terms of our thought habits, when you find yourself falling into the old habit of letting those negative thoughts (The Mean Voice) start driving the bus, catch yourself and consciously choose a different thought.

I find it helpful to the give my thought habits a name because this creates some distance between me and the thought. I'll say to myself, "Oh, here goes my brain with the 'You'll never be successful as a writer' thought loop again," and I'll consciously catch myself and *choose* to think a different (better) thought and deliberately move my attention to energizing *that* thought. I'll force myself to think, "I'm doing the very best work I can do right now and I'm proud of myself for that," and, as much as my mind wants to go back to the familiar, negative thought, I don't let it!

Like the puppy that wants to go eat the garbage on the sidewalk, I pull my brain away from that yucky thought and force it to focus on something better. Eventually, my brain does latch onto that better thought (thank you neural pathways) and then all my emotions and physiology changes in response.

Does this always work? No way! Very often I either don't catch myself in the negative thought because I'm all caught up in the fear and worry or, I wait too long to catch it by which point it's much harder to think of a more positive thought and direct your energy towards it.

However, the more you practice doing this, the better you get at it. I don't think that the negative thoughts ever stop popping into your head, but with practice you get faster and faster at catching them and better and better at redirecting your brain to a more constructive thought.

Give this a try. Start to become diligent about noticing the negative thought loops that keep popping up in your head. What you'll find is that you tend to have the same handful of negative thoughts over and over again.

For example, your Mean Voice probably rarely speaks up when you're washing the dishes. It's probably not chattering away while you're scrubbing that dirty pot and saying things like, "You're such a bad dish washer, you're never going to get this pot clean, you're so pathetic." However, try standing naked in front of the mirror or selecting an outfit for a night out with friends and see how fast it wakes up and starts to chirp at you.

I call that handful of negative thoughts that you play over and over again your brain's **"Top 10 Greatest Hits."** Start to become aware of yours and once you can identify a few of them, begin to consciously and deliberately *choose* a different, better feeling thought that you can redirect your mind towards.

The key here is to take baby steps. Don't pick a new thought that is the complete opposite of the old, negative thought because it's too big a leap and you won't really believe it. Instead, pick just a slightly better thought that you can actually believe and hold onto that for a while until you're ready to reach for a slightly better one than that. For example, don't try to leap from, "I'm fat and disgusting and I'm never going to get my eating under control," straight to "I love my body. I'm beautiful and I'm proud of who I am." It's too big of a leap and you don't believe that new thought yet. Instead, try simply moving to, "I'm grateful for many of the things my body has done for me and I'm open to the possibility that I might be able to find my way out of my current relationship with food." That feels better but it's not as big a leap from where you were and it might be something that you can sit in for a while and really start to believe.

Why Some Rewards Are so Much Harder to say "No" to Than Others

So, now that we've learned that all habits follow the same cue, behavior, reward habit loop structure, you might be wondering, why are some rewards so much more tempting than others? I do feel good after I finish a workout. So, why doesn't my brain want that as much as it wants the ice cream?

This is because, the pull of the reward is largely determined by its size and proximity. Our brains prefer immediate gratification. This phenomenon is known as "delay discounting" and we learned about it a little bit in Chapter One. Delay discounting means that the longer you have to wait for a reward, or the further away it appears, the less appealing it is to you.

Eating ice cream at night is an easy habit to create and a hard one to break because it provides an immediate and sizable reward. It's right there in your freezer and it's packed with the quick sugar and fat your brain wants. Exercising every day is a hard habit to create and an easy one to break because the reward that it provides is far away, and minimal in terms of what you can actually see right away. This is, in part, because your brain's reward system did not evolve to respond to future rewards. Remember that this part of your brain is still working in much the same way it did back in caveman days when survival was the key driver of daily life. In that context, a reward that was far off – whether 10 miles or 10 days – was pretty much useless. Later on in Part Two we're going to learn some very specific techniques you can put in place to use delay discounting to your advantage to help you disrupt old neural pathways in your brain.

Now, there's also another reason why we only seem to develop neural pathways and create habit loops around junk food and why your brain rarely craves apples or broccoli when it's stressed, tired or bored. And to understand that reason, we need to learn a bit about our good friend **dopamine**, because no exploration of our unhealthy relationship with food and cravings would be complete without talking about this key player.

Chapter 4

The Dopamine Trap

Dopamine is a neurotransmitter or chemical messenger in the brain. It plays a huge role in our cravings and was involved in the origin of many of our unhealthy habits. This is because, when we eat something like sugar or refined carbohydrates like potato chips or popcorn, dopamine is released in the brain and we get a little "high."

What's interesting, is that many people mistakenly assume that, because of that "high" it gives you, dopamine is connected to happiness and feeling good. This is not true. Dopamine is not a "feel good" neurotransmitter, it's actually a neurotransmitter that's associated with learning and motivation.

Remember and Repeat

Dopamine is released in the brain whenever you do things that are connected to survival. This includes eating highly concentrated sources of calories, feeling attracted to a mate, accumulating resources (in our modern world this can include gambling or shopping) and feeling connected to the social pack (today this often looks like scrolling through social media or watching reality TV). The dopamine that your brain releases when you do these things is responsible for helping you remember where you found them and repeating what you did to get them. Dopamine is like the marker flag your brain puts down when you do these things to help you learn that they're useful and to motivate you to return to them again and again. You can sum all that up to say that dopamine encourages you to **remember and repeat**.

When people have a dopamine deficiency, or when they lack the ability to properly absorb the dopamine that exists in their brain, we see conditions like Parkinson's where people can become almost catatonic. The lack of dopamine robs them of all motivation to act. And this is why conditions like Parkinson's are often treated with drugs like L-DOPA which increase dopamine concentrations in the brain.

So, what role does dopamine play in our cravings? Well, let's use pizza for example. According to research, pizza is consistently listed as one of people's favourite foods, something they say they crave on a regular basis. So, let's look at the role that dopamine is playing in our shared love of pizza.

Pizza is a highly concentrated source of all the elements that your brain is looking for in a food to help keep you alive (fat, starch and protein). You eat pizza for the first time and your brain thinks, "Wow, this is a phenomenal and quick source of life-giving calories and fat; we're going to want to have more of this!!"

Now, you have a lot of information coming into your brain every day and there's a lot of things for your brain to remember. There's that plumber you need to call about the downstairs bathroom, that form you need to mail in to the government, the friend you need to get back to about that thing, that supplement you heard about on Dr. Oz that you need to Google…it's a lot.

So, in order to make sure that, in the midst of all that noise, you remember this perfectly concentrated source of life-giving macronutrients that you've discovered called "pizza," your brain releases dopamine like a little Post It note to ensure that "pizza" doesn't get lost in all the other less important stuff going on in your head, and to encourage you to return to "pizza" again and again.

Dopamine does this by imprinting strongly in your mind all the cues associated with that pizza including the way it smelled, looked and tasted; the name of the restaurant and how it was decorated; the people you were with and what you were doing and how you felt. You probably have specific detailed memories of eating pizza or ice cream that you likely don't have for, say, getting the oil in your car changed.

In addition to putting down those, "remember this" markers so that you never forget pizza, dopamine also ensures you'll repeat the experience by connecting all of those mental notes with a feeling of excitement and a sort of "high." Thus, everything associated with pizza starts to feel very desirable to you. This is your brain's way of making you repeat. So, every time you notice those cues or markers again (you see pizza, smell pizza, see that restaurant, hang out with those people), your brain thinks, "Ooooh, pizza would be good!" and that's what we call a "craving."

And it's not just eating the food that gives you the dopamine hit. Once those little marker flags or Post Its are in place, there is a significant dopamine rush that comes simply from the anticipation of the reward! Thinking about what you're going to eat later in the day, planning it out in your mind, pouring the chips into the bowl, scooping out the ice cream, these all trigger the release of dopamine in your brain as well, making them almost as exciting as the eating itself and driving you towards the food even more powerfully!

I distinctly remember getting through especially stressful days at work by fantasizing about the treats I'd have later that night. I'd spend way too long walking the chip aisle at the store and standing in front of the chocolate bar display at the checkout ("No, you go ahead, I'm still looking") enjoying every moment of the delicious anticipation of what I would eat that night once everyone else was in bed and I could hit the couch with my snacks and watch my favourite TV show. The planning and anticipation were almost as good as the actual event!

So, your brain's strategy with dopamine is to plant memory markers around behaviors that contribute to your survival, and to connect those markers to feelings of excitement so you'll do them again - remember and repeat. However, your brain also starts to use this "high" that comes from the release of dopamine for another purpose and that is to complete its mission statement that we talked about earlier.

Now, because our brains are inherently wired to avoid pain and seek pleasure, when we feel pain (stress, anxiety, worry, loneliness, boredom, etc.), we immediately start to seek pleasure. Our brains have learned that when dopamine is released, it feels that "high," so, as soon as we feel bad, off we go in search of the carbs, sugar, sex, social media, or shopping that will give us a little dopamine "hit." If pizza makes me feel happy, then when I feel sad, I can eat pizza and feel happy again.

If food has been your brain's preferred dopamine-delivery system, then you've turned to food again and again when you felt down – maybe since you were a kid to get a "high." As you repeated this pattern over and over again (feel bad – eat food), a new neural pathway was formed (remember, neurons that fire together, wire together) around feeling bad and using food to feel better. Over time, this neural pathway got stronger and stronger, tighter and tighter, and was shuttled into the automatic brain and an incredibly strong habit was formed.

Now, on the surface, this might not be a total disaster. If you could feel bad, eat one cookie and feel great, that wouldn't be too terrible, right? But that's not what happens, is it?, and here's why...

The Dopamine Trap

As I explained above, many people make the mistake of thinking that dopamine is a "feel good neurochemical" but, that's not exactly true. Our brains *do* love sugar, fat, ringing slot machines and new shoes and those things do light up the dopamine receptors in our brain like a Christmas tree, but that doesn't make us feel good; that makes us feel like we're just *about* to feel good.

Remember how I explained that dopamine is actually responsible for learning and motivation (a.k.a. remember and repeat)? Dopamine is not interested in making you feel good, dopamine is interested in making you feel like you're just *about* to feel good. **Dopamine's primary function is not to make us happy, but**

52

rather to make us *pursue* happiness. Dopamine is there to get you to *act*!

This is where cravings come in. The *promise* of happiness – not the actual experience of happiness – is the brain's strategy to keep you hunting, gathering and working. If you were feeling all satisfied and content, you would stop hunting and gathering and (in caveman days) you'd probably just sit around feeling satisfied until you starved to death. Not useful.

So, when the reward system of your brain is activated, either by eating sugar, buying a new pair of shoes, or placing a bet at the blackjack table, those dopamine receptors in your brain do light up. But they're not screaming, "This feels great!" They're screaming, "Do this again! This will make you feel great!" Similar but very, very different.

Instead of feeling satisfied, content and happy, you just feel like you want *more* - that's the whole point. And this is why having one cookie when you're sad or stressed never works.

Think about it, how often, after giving in to the craving for chocolate ice cream or French fries do you feel happy, content and satisfied? Or how often, after buying the shoes or handbag do you feel like you don't want to buy anything else? Or how often, after winning a few dollars at the slot machine do you feel like you want to head off to bed? And how often do you feel guilty, anxious and like you still want more? Welcome to the **Dopamine Trap**.

And it's the Dopamine Trap that lies at the root of many of our unhealthy habits and frustrating patterns around food. Dopamine teaches your brain that food makes it feel good (or like it's just about it feel good). We then repeat that action enough times that we create neural pathways around it in our automatic brain – it becomes a habit. However, we never really get the reward we desire, so we end up constantly hunting for satisfaction. One more cookie, one more handful of chips, one more helping of lasagna. The dopamine in your brain is telling you that with just a little more you'll feel great…but you never quite get there.

Beating the Dopamine Trap

So, how do we beat the Dopamine Trap?

First, become more mindful and aware of "false reward." Start to notice when the dopamine receptors in the reward centre of your brain are calling the shots and making you *believe* that something is going to make you feel amazing, but will actually leave you feeling guilty, anxious, unsatisfied and just wanting more.

So, when you're craving the chocolate brownie so much that you can't focus on anything else, remind yourself about what's *really* going on up there. Remember, that your dopamine receptors are interested in keeping you craving, not giving you satisfaction.

And, when you do give in to the pull of dopamine, and make a choice that you're not thrilled about, and that makes you feel sick and angry with yourself afterwards, don't just try to avoid or numb those feelings or beat yourself up about it. Instead, take a moment to objectively examine and absorb the difference between how you *thought* you were going to feel by eating that thing, and how you *actually* felt. Let that really sink in for your brain - not as punishment but rather as learning.

There is growing evidence that when people pay close attention to the experience of false reward, over time, the magic spell wears off. If you force your brain to reconcile what it *expects* from a reward (happiness, bliss, satisfaction) with what it *actually* experiences (bloating, guilt, shame) your brain will eventually adjust its expectations.

Second, seek out the *real* happy neurotransmitters. Serotonin and GABA are also neurotransmitters like dopamine, but where dopamine is designed to get you to crave more, serotonin and GABA truly *are* the feel-good neurotransmitters. When these are released in the brain, you really do feel happy, calm and satisfied. They're not quite as exciting for the brain as dopamine and they doesn't make us feel the same level of craving, but they *actually* deliver what they promise.

Serotonin is produced in the brain from the amino acid tryptophan. Foods rich in tryptophan include nuts (walnuts are especially good), soy (opt for organic and minimally processed forms such as tofu, tempeh or miso), cauliflower and mushrooms. Intense sugar cravings can actually be a sign of low serotonin in the brain. In fact, those sugar cravings can actually be your brain's attempt to boost serotonin since eating sugar produces insulin in the body which helps move tryptophan to the brain.

Serotonin is also released in the brain when you engage in certain activities. Pay attention to the activities in your life that make you feel really fulfilled, grounded and content. These are usually things like: spending time with people you love, exercise, being outdoors, music, yoga, meditation, prayer, reading, creative arts, being of service to others, etc.

Since these activities are not directly associated with survival, they unfortunately don't tend to excite the brain or cause us to crave them the way dopamine-releasing activities or foods do, but they actually *do* lead to deep feelings of happiness and satisfaction. The caveman part of your brain may not connect those dots for you, but this is one of those times when your smart, modern pre-frontal cortex can often step in and over-ride the situation.

By recognizing that the junk food is just leading you into the Dopamine Trap, and by instead choosing to partake in more of these serotonin and GABA-releasing behaviors, you will reduce your brain's desire to seek out that dopamine "hit" because it will already be feeling satisfied, fulfilled and happy. No pain means no need to seek pleasure. See how the pre-frontal cortex outsmarted the caveman brain there?

And third, you can "dopamin-ize-ing" healthy behaviors and use your brain's natural love of dopamine to your advantage. This means attaching the healthy behaviors that you want to encourage, to the behaviors that give your brain that dopamine "high."

For example, if you're craving sugar, have one small square of dark chocolate (slowly and mindfully) while relaxing in a warm bath and listening to your favourite music. Or, only allow yourself to watch your favourite reality TV show when you're on the treadmill. Or, decide on a really cool, and totally frivolous, gift that you're going to buy yourself if you drink a green smoothie every day for a month.

Chapter 5

Self Sabotage

One of the questions I get asked the most by clients and members of my online community is, "Why do I keep sabotaging myself?" They can't understand why they can do so well for a few days, or even a week or two, and then blow it all in one night.

We've already talked about some of the reasons that this might happen. First, there's the fact that your brain often registers things like your stressful day, worries about your family, or even the deprivation of a diet as pain which puts it on a reward-seeking mission to move you from pain to pleasure in the most efficient way possible (sugar and fat). And that, because your limbic system, which controls that reward-seeking behavior, is so much more ingrained than your pre-frontal cortex, it almost always wins.

Second, you're dealing with that perfect storm of deep neural pathways, habit loops and your brain's love of the familiar, all of which are working to pull you back to your old ways no matter how much you might want to change.

And third, we briefly touched on how lacking a clear and compelling vision for why you want to stay on track with healthy eating and what success would truly look and feel like can make you vulnerable to external temptations and forces that can take you off track – much more on this in Part Two.

However, there also may be some other things lurking under the surface when we find ourselves sabotaging our success and it's important that we explore some of those as well.

Do you really want to lose the weight?

The answer to this question may seem ridiculously obvious. "Um, yes, more than anything in the world! Duh!" But, I'd like you to explore with me the idea that – on a subconscious level – part of you may actually not want to lose the weight.

Remember how earlier I highlighted the fact that human beings are inherently hedonistic animals. This means that we only consistently do things that work for us – that have some payoff. No payoff and we don't do it. At least, we don't continue to do it.

Long before the book and movie, *He's Just Not That Into You* came out, I remember listening to my girlfriends analyzing phone calls and voice messages (this was before the days of texting) from the latest guy they'd started dating. They'd read between the lines, consider the intonation in his voice (did he sound disappointed when he said he had to cancel their dinner to work late, or like he was lying?) and make up all kinds of possibilities and assumptions that would allow for some quantum field of reality where the fact that he cancelled again meant that he was actually madly in love with them and was just frightened by the strength of his feelings.

I had my own share of bad relationships and stupid choices when it came to men, but one thing I could always see crystal clearly was that, if he liked you he called and went out of his way to be around you, and if he didn't – he didn't. There wasn't anything to figure out. You didn't need to read between the lines. Actions say everything. People do what they want to do. If they want to be with you, they're with you. If they don't, they're not. It really is that simple. We only do things if we're getting something from it.

Now, don't get me wrong. This isn't some jaded, cynical outlook I'm offering. Human beings are often incredibly generous, and we do nice things for other people all the time. But, very often, it's in part because of how great it makes us feel to be of service and make someone else happy. That's the beautiful thing about being of service – it makes you feel so darn good!

So, when it comes to our weight and our relationship with food, we must assume that, at some level, keeping the weight on and continuing our current habits and patterns with food, offers us some kind of payoff beyond just enjoying the taste of chocolate. Here are some ideas to consider about what those might be:

The weight is protection

Sometimes having the extra padding on your body offers a feeling of safety and security. Being thinner makes you feel vulnerable and exposed. It feels harder to hide.

This can be a contributing factor for anyone, but I find that this reason can be part of the puzzle most often with people who have experienced some kind of trauma in the past, especially (but not limited to) sexual trauma. Because our society so strongly connects being healthy and fit with being sexually attractive, keeping extra weight on can help those who feel uncomfortable with the idea of being considered an object of sexual desire feel more hidden and thus safer.

The weight is familiar

As much as we may dislike what we see in the mirror every morning or how our clothes fit and feel, there is also a comfortable familiarity to all of it. We know who that person is. We know what choices she makes, what she worries about, how she copes with stress, what's expected of her and how it all turns out. It's familiar and, as we discussed earlier, your brain equates familiar with safe.

It even goes further than that because often we have an entire identity and even relationships built around the foundation of our current relationship with food and our current body size and shape. Change feels like it would require us to abandon all of that and become a different person and while that may sound very appealing to part of your brain, there's another part that struggles to imagine what we would replace it with and how that would feel. There's fear in the unknown.

We may desperately want that different body and that brain that eagerly makes the healthy choices, but at some level, becoming that person also terrifies us because we don't know who she is. More specifically, we don't know who we'd be if we were her. And that's frightening.

Maintenance appears exhausting

Losing the weight is one thing, but then, once you lose it, you have to *keep* it off! It's like that old joke, "What do you get for winning the pie-eating contest? A pie!"

When you're already overweight, there's nothing really to lose by indulging in your favourite foods or eating your feelings away. "I'm already fat!" you think to yourself. But, if you lose the weight, then you have to maintain that!

We often subconsciously conjure up an image of our future thin selves living a miserable existence of constant white-knuckling, deprivation and anxiety as our every day becomes focused on maintaining the weight loss. We imagine that we'll never again be able to enjoy our favourite foods or participate in the food-related experiences that bring us such joy and connection with the people we love. Once we've achieved our goal, there will be no room for error. All the fun will be over. Who wants that?

We've put all our eggs into the weight-loss basket

It took me a long time to write this book. Like, way longer than it should have taken. It wasn't the actual writing part that took a long time. Once I got into the rhythm of that, it only took me about a month and a half to write the whole first draft. No, it was *starting* that was my problem.

And, for the longest time, I couldn't figure out why I had so much resistance to starting. I've always loved writing. I wrote my first book (unpublished and only ever shown to my parents) when I was about 10. It was about a little girl who lived on the coast of British Columbia and the wild seal that she befriended at her local beach.

Since then, I've written another novel (also unpublished and shown to no one but my parents) as well as countless articles, poems and blog posts. Writing is my favourite way to express myself and I've always considered myself a writer before anything else. My mother is a highly acclaimed (published many times over) author and writing coach and the world of writers is something I've grown up around.

And when I considered all of that, that's when I realized why starting this book had been so hard for me. It was because it mattered so much. I wanted this so badly, that actually doing it terrified me into utter paralysis. I'd attributed so much meaning to writing this book. In my mind, once the book was out, I'd be successful. People would be helped by what I had to say, new opportunities would come flooding in and I'd basically be the person I'd always wanted to be. I'd be a writer; a *real* writer (whatever that is).

And, as long as I was always *going* to write a book, all of that was still a wonderful, shining possibility. It was all there just waiting for me in the not-too-distant future. But, what that also meant was that, if I wrote it, and failed, then all of that possibility – all of that potential – would disappear, and that was more than I could bear. So, for the longest time, I talked a whole lot about writing the book but never really started because failing at that would be too big of a failure. I had too much on the line. It was too important.

We give so much meaning to losing the weight. When we lose the weight we'll feel attractive, confident and happy. When we lose the weight we'll be calm and free and at peace. When we lose the weight we'll be healthy and immune to disease. When we lose the weight our relationships and sex lives will improve, we'll de-clutter and probably get a better job. People will like us more and we'll be funnier and smarter. We'll be like all those people we've admired for so long.

And as long as we're *going* to lose the weight, it's all still there waiting for us just over the horizon. But, here's the terrifying thing; what if we do lose the weight, and we just end up in our same old lives, with all our same old problems, feeling just as unworthy, unfulfilled and unattractive, only in a slightly smaller body? Then what?

We'd have to feel the feelings

Here's the thing, and there's really no getting around this, in order to truly be free of our old habits around food, at some point we're going to have to feel the feelings that we've been using the food to numb or avoid.

That is a terrifying prospect for your brain. That food has become your security blanket. It's the way you avoid the uncomfortable and even scary feelings that you don't want to explore. It's your treat. It's how you love yourself and make things better. It's familiar and safe. It sounds silly but, for that caveman part of your brain, giving up that safety and security feels like leaping off a cliff to certain death. Often when we talk about "cravings" what we're really talking about is the strong desire to move away from an unpleasant feeling. It's often not so much the actual food that we want, but rather the temporary escape it offers away from stress, anxiety or boredom. Avoiding those feelings is what we're truly craving.

In Part Two we're going to talk more about what it means to feel the feelings (instead of eating them) and I'm going to give you some very practical tools you can start using to do this in a way that is less terrifying for your brain and more effective at creating lasting change in your relationship with food.

So, if you're someone who has found yourself repeatedly sabotaging your success when it comes to losing weight, consider that there is some kind of payoff for that behavior. Give some thought to the suggestions I've shared above for what that payoff might be or get curious and see if it's something else entirely. Either way, it's important to acknowledge that we only continue to do things if, at some level, they're working for us. You can start asking these questions to get to the bottom of what that payoff might be for you so that you can begin to challenge those old beliefs that are keeping you stuck.

Now, self-sabotage has a dance partner and that dance partner is something called "Resistance."

Resistance

Tell me, what do think is the number one reason why you always end up sabotaging your attempts to eat better? Did you immediately think of something like: I don't have not enough time to prep and cook healthy meals, I'm not organized enough to plan ahead, I have a hard-core night-time snacking habit, I'm a picky eater, I have no willpower around carbs or I'm too lazy to stick with it?

Any of those could be true about you, but none of them are the real reason that you continue to sabotage your success. Want to know what it really is? It's something called "Resistance."

Resistance is a concept that I originally learned from reading Steven Pressfield's incredible book, *The War of Art*. In the book he defines Resistance as, "A universal force that has one sole mission: to keep things as they are."

Resistance is fueled by fear. It's that ancient caveman part of your brain that's afraid of anything that feels unfamiliar because something that's unfamiliar could mean danger and even death. Fear wants you to keep doing exactly what you've always done because that feels safe so it uses Resistance to ensure that you never change.

According to Pressfield, resistance is the force at work when you want to: write a book or a short story but never find the time, start a business but never make a plan, master a new skill but never sign up for the class, change your health and your body but never follow through.

Resistance is calling most of the shots in our lives, and we're not even aware of it and that's because Resistance isn't stupid. It doesn't say: Change is scary, or I'm afraid to give up my security blanket, or I don't know who I am if I change and that's terrifying. No, if it was that obvious, the more rational part of your brain, would quickly identify those as irrational thoughts and over-ride the Resistance.

Instead, Resistance makes excellent and compelling arguments that sound like they make so much sense. Resistance tells you that what you're trying is: too hard, too complicated, not coming at the right time, not the right approach, not working for you and your unique situation.

Resistance says:

- What the hell, you've already ruined your diet, might as well keep going;
- This is a special occasion and you won't be able to fully enjoy it unless you indulge;
- You deserve this treat right now; you can start again tomorrow or on Monday;
- You only live once, why deny yourself this pleasure?
- This doesn't feel like the right thing for you to be doing right now;
- This doesn't feel like the right approach for you. This might work for other people, but it's not the right fit for you;
- You've got so much going on right now, you'll focus on this when things quiet down.

Any of those sound familiar? Are you starting to see where Resistance might be at work in your life? Can you see where it might be sneakily sabotaging your attempts to eat better and improve your health?

So, how do you battle Resistance?

Here are three simple steps you can try to start winning the battle between your desire to reach your goals, and the Resistance that's trying to stop you.

First, become aware of it! Resistance relies on you being oblivious to what it's up to behind the scenes. As soon as you feel it at work and shine a big, bright light on it by saying, "Ah, I see you, Resistance. I see what you're up to!" it immediately begins to lose its power over you.

Second, invite it along for the ride. Accept that Resistance isn't going anywhere. It's a universal force, like gravity. However, just because you can't get rid of it, doesn't mean that you need to let it drive the bus.

In her brilliant book, *Big Magic*, Elizabeth Gilbert writes a beautiful letter to fear which I am paraphrasing here and slightly re-writing as a letter to Resistance:

Dear Resistance:

I'm about to take an important road trip that is going to result in some very big changes in my life. I understand you'll be joining me, because you always do. I acknowledge that you believe you have an important job to do in my life, and that you take your job seriously. So, by all means, keep doing your job, if you feel you must. But I will also be doing my job on this trip, which is to work hard and stay focused. There's plenty of room in this vehicle for both of us, so make yourself at home, but understand this: I am the only one who will be making any decisions along the way.

I recognize and respect that we are in this together, but please know that, despite that fact, your suggestions will never be followed. You're allowed to have a seat, and you're allowed to have a voice, but you are not allowed to have a vote. You're not allowed to touch the road maps; you're not allowed to suggest detours; you're not allowed to fiddle with the temperature. Dude, you're not even allowed to touch the radio. But above all else, my dear old familiar friend, you are absolutely forbidden to drive.

Third, celebrate *all* **progress** (even the *tiniest* of baby steps). In addition to relying on you being unaware of its actions, resistance also relies on you feeling discouraged, pessimistic and hopeless about your ability to change. That's the most fertile ground for Resistance to plant its seeds of doubt, confusion and procrastination. Those feeling are like food for Resistance! The moment you start to think that you can't do it, Resistance pounces, takes root and begins to grow like a toxic weed.

In order to counter this, it's critical that you be intentional about noticing and celebrating every shred of evidence to support the fact that you can do this. As soon as you start to notice wins and progress (no matter how tiny), you've shifted the momentum away from Resistance and put yourself back in the driver's seat!

Okay, now that we've looked at many of the reasons why what we've been trying so far (dieting, deprivation, white-knuckling, guilt, self-judgement, etc.) hasn't been working, it's time to turn our attention to what will work.

If the answer was willpower recipes or diets or carbs alone, we would have lost the weight and fixed all of our health concerns ages ago because we've tried those things for years and while we know that a lot of them work for a little bit if we stick with them, the truth is that we don't stick with them – do we? Every single time we eventually end up sabotaging ourselves and going back to our old ways.

And, as I explained, we don't stick with them because we're trying to run new behaviors on top of an old, outdated operating system in our brains, without first updating that operating system so that it matches the new behaviors. It's like trying to play a new DVD in an old VHS player. There's nothing wrong with the DVD. It might be perfectly new and it might be the best movie ever. But it will never work if you keep trying to play it in a VHS player.

There's no magic diet out there that will help you get around this fact. You could discover the absolute perfect diet, eating approach or set of quick and healthy recipes, but you will never be able to stick with it if you don't first do the work to update that old operating system. It will just keep dragging you back to your old ways again and again. So, how do we do that? How do we reprogram and rewire our old operating system so that we're playing our DVD in a DVD player and we can actually enjoy the movie?

In the next part of this book, this is exactly what we're going to tackle. I'm going to share with you much of what I've learned through my years of transforming my own relationship with food from the inside out, and helping hundreds of others do the same. I've distilled much of this learning down into five pillars that I believe hold the key to reprogramming this old "operating system" that's been keeping you stuck and in Part Two we're going to explore each one and you'll quickly start to see how you can begin to put them to work for you in your own life.

PART TWO:

What We Need to Focus on Instead

So, in Part One we learned why what we've been trying so far hasn't been working. Or at least, why it hasn't helped us reach and sustain our goals of losing weight, feeling better, or being free of our old unhealthy habits around food.

We looked at the caveman brain and its powerful mission statement, how the automatic brain works in building neural pathways that keep us repeating old behaviors, the structure of habit loops, the role of dopamine when it comes to cravings and some of the reasons behind our tendency to be our own worst enemy and sabotage our own efforts.

Now that we know what's not working, it's time to start looking at what we ought to be focusing on instead. I'm going to share with you five pillars that are each designed to work with your brain's natural wiring, rather than against it and help you go below the surface and take the steps necessary to update that old operating system, in order to create a sustainable, balanced, healthy relationship with food…and with yourself.

These are the five pillars we'll be exploring together:

PILLAR ONE: GET OUT OF AUTO-PILOT – Start living in a more mindful way each day so that you can make better understand your patterns and make more conscious and deliberate choices.

PILLAR TWO: KNOW WHERE YOU'RE GOING – Get clear and specific about the vision you have for the future you're creating for yourself.

PILLAR THREE: FEEL THE FEELINGS – Stop avoiding uncomfortable feelings like stress, boredom or even cravings; they can't hurt you and food is an ineffective way to manage them.

PILLAR FOUR: DISRUPT OLD PROGRAMMING – Update the old operating system that's driving you back to your old, familiar patterns again and again.

PILLAR FIVE: FILL YOUR CUP – Get ahead of the problem by making self-care and loving yourself a non-negotiable priority.

Let's take a closer look at each one.

Chapter 6

A Few Brief Words About Food

Before we dive into the five pillars that we need to be focusing on to truly, deeply change our relationship with food from the inside out, I want to spend just a few moments here talking about food. You may have noticed that we're now almost halfway through this book about helping you overcome overeating and we haven't actually talked about food once. Why is that?

Well, people like to joke that I'm the, "Nutritionist who never talks about food," and that's because I really do believe that the food is the easy part. Understanding what you should eat more of and what you should eat less of is actually pretty simple and something that you probably already know more than enough about. What's much harder, and what I devote one hundred percent of my focus and energy to, is helping people change the thoughts, habits and patterns that keep us making not-so-great choices over and over again.

However, that being said, I can't say nothing about food. I am a Nutritionist, I am passionate about healthy eating, and it does matter what you eat. It's going to be much harder to do the work of changing your old habits and patterns around food if you're eating a whole bunch of processed foods, sugar and chemical additives. And this is because these foods cause reactions in the body including blood sugar instability and inflammation which mask the true signals your body is sending to you about what you really need to be eating to properly fuel and nourish yourself. You'll give yourself a much better chance of succeeding with the tools and strategies you're going to learn next through the five pillars if you're limiting the processed foods and added sugars and sticking mostly to a diet of whole foods. A clean, toxin-free body is going to be much more responsive than one that is riding the blood sugar roller-coaster, lacking important nutrients and fighting inflammation.

Now, I know that there's a lot of confusing and conflicting information about nutrition out there, and that can make it feel like you don't know what you should be eating or not eating. But, while it's true that my fellow Nutritionists and I could spend hours debating differing opinions on various topics related to food, those areas that we may debate and disagree on actually represent only a tiny slice of the food conversation. The basics (the important parts) are pretty straightforward and I believe that you probably already have a much better grasp of what you need to be eating and not eating than you may think you do.

I believe that Michael Pollan said it best when he reduced it all down to: "Eat real food, not too much, mostly plants." That's it. That's really almost all there is to it. The only thing I would add to that list is: and **listen to your body**.

We get confused and distracted by all the chatter we hear out there in the press and on social media about new studies, fad diets and what the hottest celebrities are doing, but honestly we would be best served by putting blinders on to all of that and simply following those four simple rules: Eat real food, not too much, mostly plants and listen to your body.

That means, eat foods as close to their natural state as possible, meaning avoid foods containing ingredients that your grandmother would not recognize as food; eat slowly and mindfully and stop when you're satisfied; eat lots and lots of plants (veggies, fruits, beans, nuts, seeds) and let your own body tell you if it likes things like gluten, grains, dairy, eggs or soy.

We all know that you are what you eat. If you eat nutrient-poor, processed food filled with preservatives and added sugars you're going to feel it. You'll feel tired, foggy, anxious, maybe a little sad and very likely craving more and more. But, if you choose nutrient-dense, balanced, fresh, gorgeous, colourful, vibrant foods, you'll feel alive, awake, alert and increasingly free from the craving rollercoaster.

Here are the foods that should make up the majority (80% or more) of your plate:

Raw or Cooked Vegetables (especially green leafy ones)

These guys are the absolute top of the pyramid in terms of nutrition and there are so many incredible options out there that I can't possibly list them all. Eat lots of the ones you love and also be adventurous and try new ones on a regular basis. Get in as much and as many varieties as you can including a variety of colour. Aim to "eat the rainbow" every day!

Fresh or Frozen Fruits

All fresh fruits are fabulous. Berries of all kinds (strawberries, raspberries, blueberries, blackberries, etc.) are at the top of my list for a few reasons. They're packed with fiber and low in sugar which is great for people struggling with unbalanced blood sugar, which is almost everyone. They're also super high in antioxidants which help boost your immune system and reduce inflammation.

That being said, all fruits offer vitamins, enzymes and fiber and make things taste wonderful. Aim for fresh or frozen and try to avoid canned.

Fresh herbs

Not only do fresh herbs make our food taste fantastic which boosts our enjoyment while we eat, but many of them have powerful healing properties. For example, cilantro is an excellent detoxifier, mint can aid in digestion, and rosemary contains lots of great antioxidants. Try different varieties and include them in your meals whenever possible.

Spices

For thousands of years people have been using spices to, not only make food delicious, but also heal the body. Turmeric, cinnamon, ginger and cayenne are just a few of the spices that contain powerful healing properties and help with everything from digestion to blood sugar balance and even arthritis! Load up on the spices you love and seek out recipes that include spices that might be new to you.

Beans & Legumes

Beans and legumes are nutrient powerhouses. These include kidney beans, black beans, black-eyed peas, chickpeas, lentils, pinto beans and many more. They're a great source of protein, carbohydrates and fiber as well as B vitamins and even iron.

I know that a lot of people say that they can't eat beans or legumes because they trigger digestive upset (gas, bloating, etc.). If that's the case, before you give up on them entirely, I suggest that you try to gradually add them to your diet to give your system time to adjust to the increase in fiber. Start with just a tablespoon a day and steadily increase the amount over a few weeks.

Whole Grains

This includes brown rice, millet, amaranth, quinoa (not technically a grain but I'm including it here anyway) and more. Grains offer a great source of fiber, vitamins, minerals and other phytonutrients.

As with all things, listen to your body when it comes to grains. Some people feel fantastic with grains, others do not. Let your own body guide you.

Raw Nuts & Seeds

Raw, unsalted nuts and seeds like walnuts, almonds, Brazil nuts, sunflower seeds, pumpkin seeds and sesame seeds are a great source of protein and fiber and many also contain healthy fats like omega-3s that your body (and especially your brain) need to function properly. I often recommend raw nuts and seeds to my clients as a great, healthy mid-day snack. And don't forget all the amazing nut and seed butters out there!

Fermented Foods

Every day we're learning more and more about the importance of gut health to our overall well-being. Your gut (digestive system) is home to a whole ecosystem of bacteria. Some are "good" and help your body stay healthy and others – if allowed to overgrow – can contribute to many poor health conditions including allergies, eczema, joint pain, fibromyalgia and depression. Naturally fermented foods like sauerkraut, kimchi, tempeh, miso, kefir and kombucha are teeming with the "good" bacteria you want and can help balance that delicate ecosystem. Try to include some of these foods with your meals as often as possible.

Good Fats

For a long time, fats were made out to be the bad guys but we've come a long way since then. Now we know that healthy fats are an important part of our diet – especially for women. A great source of healthy fats are whole, plant-based foods including avocado, coconut and raw nuts and seeds.

Water

Every single cell and system in your body requires water to function properly. Many people are chronically dehydrated which means that they often feel tired, hungry and find themselves more susceptible to illness. You don't have to chug gallons of water every day, but do make sure that you're getting enough clean, filtered water to support your body. I personally aim for two litres a day. Try starting your day with a big glass of water and fresh lemon juice as a great way to hydrate, detoxify and alkalize the body.

These recommendations obviously don't take into account any personal allergies, intolerances or specific health challenges that you might be dealing with and you should always consult with your doctor before making any significant changes to your diet. However, I do believe that we spend far too much time worrying about and arguing over what really amount to small details when it comes to nutrition. It's not that these conversations aren't important, it's just that focusing so much on the 20 percent that is debatable distracts us from doing the 80 percent that we already know would help us.

It's like an athlete spending 80 percent of her day worrying about what shoes to wear and letting it prevent her from doing her training. Sure, shoes are important and she could probably have great debates over which ones were best, but the better use of her time would be to concentrate on what she already knows will have the biggest impact on her performance and that's training. Worry about the shoes later if you want.

So, don't get caught up in the weeds. If you're able, do your best to have the foods I've suggested above make up at least 80 percent of your plate and then do what you like with the remaining 20 percent. Fill it with high quality meat or fish, bread, pasta, dairy, Twinkies or gummy bears for all I care.

If you followed these guidelines, it's very likely that you would lose weight, notice a boost in energy and experience an improvement in your overall health. Simple, right? But I can't end the book here because I think that even though it's highly unlikely that anything I've said above is news to you, it's not helpful because you still struggle to do it consistently, right?

That's why even though I'm passionate about healthy eating, I've dedicated only this short chapter to talking about the actual food. Because I think you already *know* what the healthier choice is in most situations. What you want to learn is how to make that choice more consistently and without feeling deprived.

So, let's move on and talk about what I think will be much more useful for you and that is detailed, science-based strategies for reprogramming and rewiring the old patterns and habits – what I call your old "operating system" – around food so that making those healthy choices starts to feel a whole lot easier. Sound good? Okay, then let's move on!

Chapter 7

PILLAR ONE: Get out of Auto-Pilot

I truly believe that our biggest enemy when it comes to creating new, healthier eating habits that feel sustainable is not our love of sugar or carbs or our lack of time or quick and easy recipes. I believe that our single biggest enemy is the state we know as "auto-pilot."

Auto-pilot is what we fall into when we've repeated an action or thought so many times that our brain has developed strong enough neural pathways around it that we can now do it without even thinking. It's simply become automatic.

In the first part of this book we talked about how your brain is always striving to automate behaviors and that, as soon as you repeat something a few times in the same way, your brain will form neural pathways around it, eagerly shuttle it into the automatic mind and create a habit around it so that it can free up energy to deal with more immediate issues.

This is great for things like walking, chewing, smiling and even tying your shoes (it would seriously cut into our daily productivity if we had to consciously think about how to do each one of those things every time we did them). But this is incredibly problematic when find ourselves wanting to change some of those old habits and patterns that are no longer serving us.

Your brain is designed to rely heavily on auto-pilot. It's set up to automate and create habits around as many tasks and behaviors as it possibly can. And, since it assumes that you would only repeat behaviors that were important and valuable, once it's automated one of those behaviors, it will strongly resist giving it up or allowing it to change in any way.

This means that if we do want to make some changes, we have an uphill battle ahead. If we want to get into the automatic brain and start ripping up some of that old wiring, we must resist auto-pilot as often as possible. Because, every time you fall into auto-pilot, you're falling into old habits. Every time you allow auto-pilot to drive, you're handing the reins over to the old patterns that got you to where you are now.

It's not easy to resist. Because of how heavily your brain relies on it, auto-pilot is dangerously seductive. It feels so much easier to simply do what you always do. It requires no thought. There's no resistance. It's effortless. And, in a world where we're increasingly stressed, overwhelmed, sleep deprived and not feeling our best, giving in to the ease of auto-pilot feels all the more tempting.

Alternatively, pulling yourself out of auto-pilot and being awake, conscious and aware of what you're thinking and doing, can feel hard. It's foreign and uncomfortable and when we're already so often feeling tired and overwhelmed by life, it can feel like more than we can handle.

How often have you been guilty of knowingly slipping back into old habits just because it's easier? You see yourself doing it, but it just feels too hard to stop yourself. You tell yourself, "I don't have the energy right now. I'll enjoy my chips in front of the TV tonight and do better tomorrow." Well, you are not alone!

We do this partly because making the non-familiar choices feels hard, but also partly because we feel that, if we become more aware, awake and honest about the way we're using food in our lives, then we'll have to face the things we're using food to avoid and give up our protective security blankets, and that is something that we do not feel prepared to deal with right now. Sound about right?

But here's the thing: Just because you become aware and conscious of something does not mean that you need to change it in the same moment. Those can be two different steps. Becoming aware is a requirement for taking action to change, but the action does not need to happen at the moment that you become aware. Those two things need not be done simultaneously.

At the end of the day, no matter how familiar, attractive and comfortable auto-pilot feels, if we don't break out of it, we will not be able to create change in our lives. It's that simple. You can't break old habits, change old patterns or create a new relationship with food while in auto-pilot. We must figure out a way to break the trance.

Magic Moments

Before we get into *how* you go about moving from auto-pilot into greater awareness, I want to touch on another reason why doing the work to spend less time in auto-pilot and cultivate more presence and intentionality in your life can be so powerful and transformative.

Austrian neurologist, psychiatrist and Holocaust survivor, Viktor Frankl said that, "Between stimulus and response there is a space. In that space is our power to choose our response. In our response lies our growth and our freedom."

What he meant was that, between the time that something happens (a situation, an interaction with someone else, a thought in your own head), and your response (feeling a certain way, saying something back, turning to food), there's a space – a moment.

It's a moment that, when we're in auto-pilot, we tend to blow right past. We don't even see it. Our response feels automatic and sometimes even barely within our control, but it's not. That moment – the moment between stimulus and response - exists every single time and it's actually a magical place bursting with potential. It's the place where all your power resides. The place where the potential to change the trajectory of your life and your health is fully available to you. It's in that moment that you choose – consciously or unconsciously – to repeat old habits and patterns, or to do something different.

I talk to my students a lot about "intentional living" and what that means. The truth is that most of us are living our lives almost entirely in auto-pilot. From the thoughts we have when we first open our eyes in the morning, to the way we respond to pressures at work, to the way we interact with the people around us, to the way we use food to cope, so much of it has simply become automatic. We do the same things, think the same thoughts, and repeat the same habits today that we did yesterday and that we'll do again tomorrow. And then we sit around and feel frustrated and angry with ourselves for not changing.

I want you to know that the potential and power to change is waiting for you in those magic moments between stimulus and response – between experience and reaction. Moments that can happen in such a flash that we miss them again and again and end up feeling helpless. I call these "magic moments" because of the incredible potential they possess to allow us to reprogram our old operating system and literally become a different person.

I encourage you to try to notice those magic moments. See if you can catch that tiny, almost invisible gap between when something happens or a thought pops into your head, and you react by feeling a certain way or moving towards food to cope. They happen so fast that you almost can't catch them – but they're there and the more you look for them, the more you'll start to see them.

Slow down. Bring your attention into the present. Become aware of yourself, your thoughts and your actions. Find the moment. Find the gap. Choose to over-ride your auto-pilot program. That's when true transformation begins. When you become aware of these magic moments over and over again in your day, you will start to feel the magnificent power they offer you to start truly changing your life.

Okay, so let's dive into how we can leverage these magic moments to start spending less time in auto-pilot and more time in awareness where all our power for change lies.

How do we wake up out of auto-pilot?

Auto-pilot is a habit. Just like all the other habits that are waiting for you when you're in auto-pilot, slipping into the state of auto-pilot itself is a habit. It's familiar and comfortable and we go there without even thinking about it, which means that breaking that habit, doing something different, choosing to be awake and intentional more often is going to be a bit hard a first. It's going to require you to keep remembering to do it and it's going to mean resisting the comfort of zoning out.

But that's the price of change I'm afraid! The good news is that, as with anything, the more you practice being conscious, awake and aware, the easier it will start to feel. If you keep doing it, even though it's hard at first, being present and curious will more and more become your natural default the more you do it.

Usually our awareness only kicks in *after* we've made a not-so-great choice (we beat ourselves up, promise ourselves we'll do things differently on Monday, etc.) but *during* the act we're zoned or spaced out – we're in auto-pilot. Our goal here is to eventually become aware of our triggers *before* we fall into old habits so that we can consciously make a better choice, but to start, just work on being more aware and curious *during*, or even *after* an indulgence.

Our goal here is to move from being aware after, to being aware during, to being aware before. Here are a few key ways we can start to make that shift:

Replace judgement with curiosity.

The easiest way to start moving yourself out of auto-pilot is simply to become curious. It's almost impossible to be both in auto-pilot and curious at the same time. Ask questions all the time.

Why do I want this?

Why do I *really* want this?

How am I hoping this food will make me *feel?*

Is there anything I'm trying to avoid or escape (a feeling perhaps)?

What was I doing, how was I feeling, what was I thinking right *before* I decided to eat this?

How did I justify this choice to myself?

How am I afraid I'll feel if I don't *eat* this?

We spend an awful lot of time judging ourselves and beating ourselves up for the choices we make around food and our health. I think, on some level, we feel like we need to keep beating ourselves up and punishing ourselves, so that we don't go crazy and eat even more!

But we couldn't be more wrong about this. As we saw in Part One, this actually has the opposite effect that we want because your brain registers that nasty internal judgement as pain and immediately sends you searching for something pleasurable to get away from it. This means one more bowl of ice cream or another handful (or five) of those chocolate-covered-pretzels. Further, when we're busy judging ourselves we can't get curious and gather any useful information about the real reasons behind why we made the choice we made. We can't learn anything that might help us next time.

Replacing our nasty self-judgement with curiosity is the best way to start becoming more aware of what's actually going on when it comes to our relationship with food. This is where we collect the data we need to begin to understand, and eventually predict and change, our habits and patterns around eating.

Judgement brings you nothing but unhappiness and more bad choices. Curiosity brings you information, awareness, clarity and the power to change.

"I just love ice cream."

My mother and I recently took a day trip to a lovely little lavender farm near her home. As with any good tourism business, the final stop on the tour was the gift shop. The shop was filled with lavender oils, lotions, soaps, jams, cookies and pillows. Anything you could put lavender into was in this shop.

As soon as you walked in the smell of lavender was overwhelming. One of the shop clerks smiled at me as I was taking it all in and I said to her, "Wow, it smells so nice in here; you must love smelling this all day," to which she replied, "Oh, you don't even notice it any more after a few minutes."

Even if you've never heard the word "habituation," it's something that I know you've experienced. Habituation is the phenomena by which the more we're exposed to a stimulus, the less we respond to it. This is what was happening for those lavender shop clerks. The first few minutes at work smelled delightful, but then very quickly, they couldn't smell it anymore.

The same is true with food. This is why the first few bites of something delicious tastes utterly amazing but all the bites after that, while still good, are far less thrilling.

Often students will say to me, "I just love ice cream. There's no other reason I'm eating it. I just love it and so I can't stop and I always want more."

However, taste mapping studies show that it's only during the first one to three bites of any food that you truly taste something you enjoy. After that, your brain normalizes the flavour and the pleasure you feel drops substantially. So, it's not the taste that keeps us coming back for more; there's something else going on there. Get curious about what that something is. Part of waking up out of auto-pilot is becoming aware and noticing, with each bite, whether the taste is still worth it, or whether you're just eating more in the hopes of getting back to how wonderful those first few bites were. The only way to know this is to be awake and aware with each bite.

Also, let's just talk for a moment about this notion of loving something. When you truly love something, don't you want to be fully present for it? Don't you want to enjoy every bit of it? If you love someone, and you only get to see them every now and then, don't you want to spend that time fully present with them? But that's not what we tend to do with foods that we claim to love. Usually the foods that we claim to love are eaten at break-neck speed while zoned out in front of the TV or iPad. That doesn't feel like love to me. That feels like something else. Getting out of auto-pilot is going to help you figure out what that something is.

Start listening to your body and speaking its language again

Decades of dieting have made us incredibly good at ignoring and disregarding the messages and signals our body is sending us. Dieting teaches us that our body is the enemy and never to be trusted. If you're hungry, ignore it. If you're craving something, ignore it. After years of practicing that we've gotten really good at it. It's become automatic!

Getting out of auto-pilot means re-opening the lines of communication between your brain and your body. You must learn how to speak your body's language again. It's like getting reacquainted with an ex. You used to know how to communicate. At one time you could finish that person's sentences, but then you spent a long time not speaking and now you're a little rusty. Now you need to re-learn their body language, facial expressions and undertones. It's the same now as we seek to re-learn the way our body speaks to us.

As often as you can, stop what you're doing, take a deep breath, tune in and see what's going on in there. How are you feeling? Where are you holding tension? Does anything hurt? What's warm? What's cold? Where do you notice sensation? Where do feel nothing?

A great little exercise to do here is a simple **body scan**. You can do this at home on the couch, at work in a chair, lying in bed before you go to sleep, or even while you're riding the bus or on an airplane.

Start by simply bringing your attention down to your toes. How do they feel? Go from toe to toe on each foot. Notice anything? Next, move through the rest of your foot and up your ankles. What do you feel there? Tight? Sore? Cold? Stiff? Then move your attention up your calves and around your knees. What's going on there? And in this way, you move all the way up to the crown of your head, exploring every part of your body and, without judging anything as good or bad, just get used to the practice of *noticing* what's going on.

Now, as we know, communication is a two-way street. If your body is going to start letting you in and sharing with you how it's feeling, you can't just keep ignoring it. That's not a foundation for a healthy relationship. In order to keep up your part of the bargain here you need to start respecting and honouring it when it asks for things. Feed it whole, nutrient-dense food when it's hungry. Move it in new ways (our bodies were designed to move). Let it rest when it wants to rest.

"But what it wants is to sit on the couch all day and eat Pop Tarts!" I hear you say.

No, it does not. There isn't one part of your body that wants that. The thing that wants to sit on the couch all day and eat Pop Tarts is your brain. More specifically, that little part of your brain that has formed neural pathways around using food as a way to manage uncomfortable feelings. That's what wants to sit on the couch and eat Pop Tarts and the better you get at using those cravings as an opportunity to tune in and get curious about what your beautiful body *truly* wants, and honouring those needs, the quieter that little part of your brain will become.

Am I really hungry?

One of the first things we lose when we stop speaking our body's language is our awareness of when we're hungry and when we're satisfied.

I can't tell you how many of my students tell me that they genuinely struggle to know whether they are hungry or not. And, while understandably frustrating, this makes perfect sense. When you've spent years and years ignoring your body and not trusting any of the messages it's sending you about what you should eat, how much or when, it makes sense that you'd eventually start to lose the ability to hear those messages.

Imagine growing up to the age of 12 speaking one language, only to move to a whole new country on your 12th birthday where you learned to speak a completely different language. If you then, as an adult, suddenly decided to travel back the country of your birth, you would likely get off the plane and struggle to understand the locals who were speaking to you. There might be familiar-sounding words or phrases, but for the most part, you'd be lost. This is what happens when we start dieting at a young age and then, decades later, attempt to start listening to our body's signals and messages again.

A tool that can be very helpful as you begin the process of re-learning your body's language around hunger and fullness, is to think of where you are on a simple hunger scale which looks something like this:

1 – Ravenously hungry. Almost panicked or a little light-headed. Can think of very little other than how you can find something to eat.

2 – Uncomfortably hungry. You would really, really like something to eat now please.

3 – A little hungry. Having something to eat sounds pretty good but you could also wait if you needed to.

4 – Neutral. You feel neither hungry nor full. Eating isn't on your mind at all.

5 - Satisfied but still feeling light.

6 – Full. You know you don't need to eat any more.

7 – Uncomfortably full. You know you ate too much.

8 – Absolutely stuffed. Your pants feel tight, your stomach may even hurt a bit and you feel sick at the idea of eating another bite.

Each time you eat, think about where you started on this scale, notice as you move along it and note where you're at when you stop eating. The more you pay attention and use this tool, the more you'll be able to associate different physical feelings with where your body is at on this hunger scale and the better you'll get at knowing where you are on the scale automatically, without having to think about it.

Another test I like to use is what I call "**The Apple Test**." Very often we confuse our desire to use food to alter the way we're feeling with actual physical hunger. A good way to find out if you're using food for fuel or for feelings is to remove as much of the enjoyment and excitement around the food as possible so that you can get a clearer picture. You can do this by imagining that someone was offering you an apple.

While delicious, an apple is not typically high on the list of foods that people crave. So, the next time you feel like you want to eat, ask yourself whether or not an apple would be amazing right now. If the answer is yes, then you probably truly are hungry. But if instead you think, no, I'm not really feeling like an apple right now, then you're likely looking to use food as a way to do something other than addressing true physical hunger at which point you need to get curious about what you're really hoping the food will do. Or, more importantly, how you're hoping the food will make you feel.

Meditation

Meditation is the most powerful tool we have for getting better at being awake, aware and mindful. Sitting in stillness, letting your mind wander and bringing it back to a specific focus like the breath over and over again eventually teaches your mind to do that more easily and more often throughout the rest of your day. This allows you to notice things about how and why you do things that you may have otherwise been unaware of. And when you're unaware of something, it's almost impossible to change it.

I like to think of it as a kind of workout for your brain, a way to strengthen your "mindfulness muscle" and spend less time in auto-pilot. If you wanted to strengthen your bicep muscle, for example, you'd do sets of bicep curls a few times a week for several weeks or months, after which time, if you'd been consistent in your workouts, you'd start to notice that your biceps were getting stronger. The same thing is taking place when you meditate. As you're sitting in meditation, every time your mind wanders and you notice that it's wandered and gently bring it back to focus on your breath, you've done one "rep" in your mindfulness workout. The more sets of these reps you do, the stronger your mindfulness muscle is going to get.

Meditation also helps you strengthen your "observer" muscle. It allows you to start to observe your thoughts. This is important because it's our thoughts that create or emotions and it's typically emotions that drive our food choices. When you begin to observe your thoughts, you start to understand that you are not your thoughts; you are the *creator* of your thoughts. And that's a pretty massive thing to realize (like, life-changing).

For all of these reasons, meditation is the perfect tool to help us explore what's really going on with us when it comes to food and begin to forge new patterns and habits.

Meditation is not a religion. It's not about turning your brain off and it's not about entering some mystical state of enlightenment (usually). It's also not about having zero thoughts so don't worry that you can't meditate simply because your mind is full of thoughts. Everyone's mind is full of thoughts and everyone can meditate.

How to meditate

All you need to do is find 5 – 30 min in which you won't be disturbed. Set a timer, sit down in a quiet and comfortable place. It doesn't need to be an ashram or Zen garden. It could be your couch, your car in in a parking lot, or your bathroom floor if that's the only quiet place in your life. I don't suggest you meditate lying down since it's too easy to fall asleep and sleep and meditation are not the same thing.

Get comfortable - preferably with a straight spine - close your eyes and bring your focus to your breath. You don't need to breathe in any fancy way or chant or say "om." Breathe the way you normally do and just bring your attention to the breath coming in and then the breath going out.

When your mind wanders (and it will, over and over again), just notice that your mind has wandered and bring it back to your breath. When your brain starts telling you that you're doing it wrong and you're not feeling something you're probably supposed to be feeling, notice that you're thinking, let those thoughts go like clouds moving across a blue sky and bring your attention back to your breath.

When you feel frustrated because you can't stop the thoughts from coming, and you can only keep your mind on your breath for a few seconds before it slips away again to your To Do lists and more judgement about the fact that you suck at this meditation thing and are definitely doing it wrong, just notice that your brain is thinking all of that, let it go and bring your attention back to your breath.

When your 5-30 min is up and your timer goes off, open your eyes. There, you just meditated - perfectly!

I like to use the analogy of training a puppy. If you were to decide that you wanted to train a puppy to sit, you'd tell the puppy to sit. She'd sit...for about two seconds, and then she'd be up running around the room and sniffing everything. When this happened, you wouldn't yell at the puppy, you'd simply pick her up, tell her to "sit" again and put her back in that "sit" position. She'd sit there for maybe four seconds this time, and then up she'd get again, chewing and jumping all over the place. You wouldn't, based on that experience, decide that your puppy was "untrainable." You wouldn't say, "I guess this just isn't the kind of dog that sits." No, you'd understand that, with some time, patience, and consistent repetition, eventually the puppy would learn how to sit for longer and longer periods of time.

It's exactly the same with training your brain to bring its focus from what you're making for dinner, back to your breath. It just takes time, patience and consistent repetition. The most important thing is that you be consistent with your practice, and gentle with yourself. With enough time and practice, just as with anything, your brain will get better and better at controlling its thoughts and you'll find yourself automatically reacting to things far less.

When should you meditate?

Whenever works best for your schedule. I like to meditate first thing in the morning to set the stage for my day in an intentional and deliberate way, but if you prefer to do it at lunch, or at the end of the day, go ahead!

Where should you meditate?

Wherever you can sit for 5-30 minutes in a comfortable position where you won't be in pain, get too distracted or fall asleep.

How often should you meditate?

Ideally meditation will be a daily practice, however, if you can only do it a few days a week, then do that!

What if you "can't" meditate?

Everyone can meditate. Yes, even you. And, there's some evidence that suggests that people who find that their mind wanders excessively during mediation, actually get more benefit from the practice than those who are able to hold their focus more easily.

The reason for this is the workout analogy I shared earlier. Every time your attention wanders and you gently bring it back to your breath, you're doing one "rep" in your "mindfulness muscle" workout and just like at the gym, the more reps, the greater the benefit!

Mindful Eating

There's a lot of talk in magazines and online these days about mindful eating. But what is it exactly and why is it something we should be thinking about or adopting in our own lives?

Simply put, mindful eating is a way to use mindfulness to help us pay attention to why, when and how we're eating so that we can gain more control over the choices we make when it comes to food.

Mindful eating allows you to slow down and reconnect with your body and the subtle signals it's sending you all the time about when it's truly hungry, when it's had enough food, and what foods work best for it. It also allows you to start addressing the real reasons behind unhealthy habits such as emotional eating, and night-time binges that may have been sabotaging you and preventing you from reaching your goals.

Mindful eating is basically a way of eating that is the exact *opposite* of the way most of us eat now. When we eat mindfully, we don't stand at the counter, scroll through our phones, watch TV, work on the computer, or clean up the kitchen. We just eat, nothing else. We sit down at a table. We notice the food that we're eating – the way it looks, smells, and tastes. We take our time and become aware of how we feel as we eat. We appreciate the food and everyone who helped it get to our plates. We chew slowly and listen to the messages from our body about when we've had enough.

Whether it's overwhelming cravings, emotional eating, or night-time bingeing, mindful eating is one of the most powerful tools we have in our toolbox to help us take back control. If you aren't convinced yet, here are just a few ways that eating mindfully can help you truly transform your relationship with food:

You're less likely to overeat

When you slow down and bring your focus to the act of eating, you start to actually notice how you feel while you're eating. This gives your body the time it needs to realize how much you've eaten and you will start to feel full long before you can eat all those unnecessary extra calories.

A box of Girl Guide cookies is easy to inhale while sitting in front of the TV, mindlessly stuffing one after another into your mouth until your hand hits the bottom of the empty box. But, try turning off the TV, moving to the dining room table and emptying that same box of cookies onto a plate and sitting down to eat them. I promise you they won't be nearly as appetizing, and you'll very likely enjoy just one or two before feeling satisfied and leaving the rest.

Very often, when people start to eat more mindfully, they are shocked by how little they need to eat before they feel satisfied. Weight loss can often come, not from focusing on *what* we're eating, but rather on how we're eating it.

Your digestion improves

Your nervous system has two settings: sympathetic and parasympathetic.

The sympathetic nervous system is triggered by stress. It's your "fight or flight" state and you don't need to be running away from a bear for your "fight or flight" response to be triggered. Your body will shift into this state in response to any perceived stress such as traffic, work deadlines, challenging people, financial worry, etc. Digestion takes a back seat when your sympathetic nervous system is engaged and since this is where the majority of us spend most of our lives, the result is widespread symptoms of poor digestion including bloating, gas, indigestion, acid reflux and feeling sleepy after a meal.

Your parasympathetic nervous system, on the other hand, is relaxation-induced. We call this your "rest and digest" state. It's what kicks in when you feel calm and peaceful and it's the state in which your body is ready and able to digest and absorb nutrients from food.

If you're always eating on the run, or while multitasking at work, or arguing with your kids, your body is engaging the sympathetic nervous system and you are not digesting food properly or absorbing the nutrients from what you're eating.

When you begin to eat more mindfully you slow down and relax, triggering your parasympathetic nervous system. Your body is then better able to break down the food and very often this means that your digestion improves and symptoms such as bloating, gas and indigestion disappear.

You make better choices

When we're eating mindlessly, we tend to make much poorer choices than we would if we were paying attention.

How often have you been at a party, or other social situation, surrounded by not-so-great food choices and found yourself eating things, not because you even wanted them, but just because they were there and you weren't paying attention? I'm pretty sure we've all been guilty of this.

When we're awake and present, we're much better able to mindfully consider the options in front of us and make a conscious choice that won't leave us feeling stuffed and ill later on.

You enjoy your food more

People often tell me that they struggle to resist certain foods because they just love them so much. But, as I mentioned earlier, if you really love something, do you experience it while zoned out in front of the TV, scrolling through your phone, or rushing around the house? Not usually.

When you love something, you want to take your time with it, enjoying and savouring every moment of it.

When you're eating mindlessly in front of the TV, and only notice what you've eaten when you hit the bottom of the potato chip bag, you can't really say that you're enjoying it. However, when you're fully present with your food, engaging all of your senses in the experience, and fully present for every bite, now you *really* get to appreciate and enjoy the food you're eating.

You start to learn which foods are best for you

There's a lot of debate in the nutrition world about which foods are good and which are bad. Should you eat dairy or not? More fat or less? Grains? Gluten? Meat? Eggs? Soy? The truth is that the answers are different for everyone. Only your body can tell you what foods work best for you and which do not. And the answers may change from day to day, season to season and year to year.

When you start eating mindfully and really *listening* to your body, you begin to notice patterns around which foods your body really enjoys, and which ones leave you feeling tired, foggy and bloated.

This allows you, over time, to tailor your diet to perfectly fit you, regardless of what the latest media report claims.

You don't find yourself eating your feelings

Do you ever find yourself craving sugary or fatty foods when you're stressed, tired or bored? Do you ever get through a stressful day by looking forward to the food you'll eat later than night? Very often our food choices are a direct result, not of what our bodies need for nutrition, but rather how we're feeling.

When you become more mindful of your eating habits, you naturally begin to pay more attention, not only to what you're eating, and how much, but also to *why* you're eating. You start to tune in – even before you start eating – and asking yourself, "Am I truly hungry right now?" or "What am I really hoping this food will do for me right now?" These questions help you better understand the reasons behind your cravings, which gives you more power to begin to free yourself from them. Where you used to mindlessly eat when you were stressed, anxious or bored, now you will begin to recognize those patterns and be in a position to change them.

5 Simple Mindful Eating Exercises

I want to give you five very specific and practical mindful eating exercises that you can start trying out immediately. You can start implementing them all at once, or experiment with them one at a time, adding a new one each day or each week until they all become part of your regular routine around food.

They're simple to understand. You can do them anywhere and at any time. And they don't require any extra tools, money or expertise. Moreover, if you begin to implement them consistently, I promise you that the impact on your relationship with food will be profound. The more consistently you use them, the bigger the impact will be in your life.

1. Stop Multitasking

These days we're all chronic multitaskers, and our eating habits are no exception. We eat in the car. We eat while we're working. We eat while watching TV and scrolling through our phones at the same time. And this habit is having a disastrous effect on our digestion, our waistlines, and our overall health.

The truth is that our bodies can only properly digest food or absorb nutrients when they're in a relaxed state; multi-tasking is not a relaxed state. Moreover, when we aren't paying attention when we're eating, we are extremely vulnerable to overeating because we're not tuned into the signals our bodies are sending us saying that we're full!

Try choosing at least one meal or snack a day and eat it sitting down and doing nothing but eating. Consider where this food came from and allow a moment of gratitude for the people and animals that were involved in bringing it to you. Observe your body while you eat. Use all of your senses. Notice how the food looks, smells, tastes and feels in your mouth. Notice how it feels physically when you're chewing and swallowing. Notice how it feels in your stomach. Notice how your energy and moods change after you eat. Turn your attention inward and just be aware of what's going on (no judgement allowed).

☐

2. Slow Down

Most of us tend to eat way too fast and this results in mindless eating, poor digestion and chronic overeating. Like multitasking, eating too quickly makes it very difficult for your body to digest your food properly, absorb the nutrients in that food, or recognize when it's had enough.

By slowing down we engage the parasympathetic nervous system so that we can improve digestion, allow the nutrients we require to be properly absorbed by the body and open up the time and space we need to tune in to how the food is making us feel and when we should stop eating.

Make a conscious effort to slow down when you're eating. As often as possible, notice when you're eating very quickly, and force yourself to do the opposite. To do this, you might try putting your fork down between bites or just taking one or two conscious deep breaths between bites. Don't be in such a rush. Take your time. Relax and enjoy your food.

3. Chew More

Chewing is one of the very first – and most important – phases of the digestive process and most of us don't do nearly enough of it.

When you're chewing you're signalling to your stomach that food is coming so that it can begin to secrete all the digestive juices it needs like hydrochloric acid and various digestive enzymes. When you swallow big chunks of food without chewing properly you're making your stomach and other digestive organs work much harder than they're meant to. This leads to indigestion, burping, bloating and that feeling of heaviness and sleepiness that we have after eating a meal that we haven't digested well.

Doing more chewing is also another way to help you slow down the eating process which, in turn, gives you time and space to be more mindful and aware of how your body is feeling and when you've had enough.

When you're eating, make a point of chewing *twice as much* as you normally would. Then, when you feel like you've chewed forever – chew a little more. It will feel strange, and perhaps even a little uncomfortable at first because we each have a habit and a rhythm around how we chew. Changing that will feel awkward, but if you continue to be aware and consistently try to increase the amount that you chew, eventually you will develop a new rhythm around chewing more. Soon this will begin to feel natural and comfortable, and will do your digestion and overall health a world of good.

4. Listen to Your Body

Your body knows, better than me, better than your friends, and better than any magazine article, what types of foods work best for it and how much it needs to eat. And, all day long it's sending you subtle signals about all of this. The problem is that for many years most of us haven't been listening. And now, when we do want to start listening again, we find that we no longer understand our body's language.

If you've ever been on a diet, you know that the whole intention behind dieting is to train yourself to *ignore* the signals your body is sending you. If you're hungry, ignore it. If you're craving something, ignore it. What this means is that many of us have spent years practicing the art of ignoring our bodies. As a result, we've gotten really, really good at it. So good in fact, that now, when we find ourselves wanting to tune inward and listen, we can find it very difficult.

As often as you can, practice tuning in to those subtle signals your body is sending you. When you first feel that desire to eat something, check in with your body and ask if you're really, physically hungry (think of the hunger scale or the Apple Test we talked about earlier), or emotionally hungry (i.e., you're bored, stressed, anxious, etc.), or caught up in a craving (i.e., you must have those potato chips in the cupboard, or the ice cream in the freezer).

When you're eating, slow down, be present, chew, focus on the food and pay attention after each bite. Really tune in to how your body is feeling and when it feels satisfied (not full, but satisfied). Give yourself permission to stop mid-meal if your body says it's no longer hungry (give the rest away or put it in a doggie bag or in the fridge for delicious leftovers tomorrow).

I think you'll be surprised by how much you learn, and how much more intuitive you become about eating, once you practice listening to your body for a little while.

☐

5. Indulge Mindfully

Constant deprivation always eventually leads to self-sabotage - always.

As human beings, food is a source of enjoyment for us. It's pleasurable for our brains, our bodies and our souls. When we repeatedly tell ourselves that we can't have something, our brains register that constant deprivation as pain and eventually go searching for pleasure to end that pain.

To avoid this, we want to start working *with* our natural, biological attraction to food, but we want to do it in a controlled, mindful and meaningful way. Simply inhaling everything in sight because we're so sick and tired of struggling to avoid it is not a helpful approach. Instead, we want to indulge *mindfully*. We want to keep our brains happy by having the foods they crave, but we want to do it in a manner that honours the needs of our bodies.

When you find yourself at the party or restaurant or at work at 3 o'clock in the afternoon, and there's a plate of chicken wings or a donut that is calling to you so loudly that you can't concentrate on anything else, have it, but be incredibly mindful as you do.

First, stop, take a breath and tune into what's *really* going on inside. Why do you want this food so badly? Is it because you know it will be delicious? Is it because of what's going on around you? Is it because you're exhausted, drained and feel empty physically and emotionally and you know a sweet or crunchy treat will make you feel good? No judgement allowed here, and don't try to change the situation at this point, for now just practice becoming aware of it.

Next, have the thing you want so badly, but follow these rules: You must eat it slowly, and with as little multitasking as possible. You must chew twice as much as you normally would. You must not allow judgement to creep in. You must listen to your body and stop the instant you feel satisfied. You must feel gratitude, appreciation, and joy with every bite.

PILLAR ONE: Get Out of Auto-Pilot
TRY THIS

Look for the Magic Moments. Try to notice these tiny gaps between when something happens or a thought pops into your head, and you react by feeling a certain way or moving towards food to cope. So much power lies in these moments that it's worth trying to find yours.

Practice being more aware. Pull yourself out of auto-pilot as often as you can and notice what you're doing, how you're feeling and what you're thinking before, during and after eating. You don't even need to change anything yet, just practice being aware.

Replace judgement with curiosity. There is no value in judgement. All the data you need to make real change will come from getting curious. Try to notice when you've slipped into self-judgement and choose to move into curiosity instead.

Keep reminding yourself about habituation. When you're craving more, remember that the fifth, sixth and seventh bite will never taste as good as the first three did.

Start listening to your body and learning to speak its language again. You can do this by checking in with it regularly throughout the day. Try doing the simple body scan exercise a few times a day or even just before you fall asleep at night.

Use the Hunger Scale and Apple Test. If you struggle with knowing whether you're truly hungry or not, consult the Hunger Scale before, during and after eating and start to notice how your own body feels in each of these phases. Also try asking yourself if an apple would be amazing right now. If it wouldn't then you're likely not physically hungry. Get curious about what else might be going on.

Start a daily meditation practice. This is the very best way to begin to strengthen your "mindfulness muscle." Start with just 5 minutes every day and slowly work your way up. If you're new to meditation, try some of the many free apps that are available or search YouTube for free guided meditations.

Eat mindfully at least once a day. Start to be more awake, aware and present when you're eating. Stop multitasking, slow down, chew more, listen to your body and indulge in the foods you love mindfully.

Chapter 8

PILLAR TWO: Know where you're going

When we want to achieve specific goals, we generally get very focused on our *behaviors*. Another way of saying this is that when we're not happy with our outcomes, we tend to put all of our attention on our actions. For example:

"If I want to be in better shape, I need to work out more."

"If I want to lose weight, I need to eat less."

"If I want to stay on track with healthy eating, I need to plan healthy meals and batch cook on the weekends."

We're focused on what we're *doing* (or not doing). This is the approach that pretty much everyone out there is following but it doesn't seem to be working too well, does it? Hundreds of millions of people are taking this approach and feeling frustrated by the fact that they're not able to reach their goals. And their solution to that tends to be to recommit and double down even more on doing the things they need to do.

But the question is, if we believe that changing our behaviors will help us get the results we want, and we really do want to make those changes so we can get those results, then why is it so hard to do it?

We've already talked about the role that neural pathways, habit loops, the Dopamine Trap and self-sabotage play in all of this, but there's something else going on here that we need to touch on. And it might actually be the biggest missing piece of the puzzle.

The truth is that the reason you struggle to do the things you want to do is because, right now, you're not the kind of person who does those things. Those things do not align with your current

100

identity. Let me explain.

Behavior → Result

This is what most people are focused on.

I do a behavior (I sit on the couch when I should be at the gym, I eat potato chips for dinner when I should be eating salad), and I get a result (I gain weight, I'm exhausted all the time).

What they do then is try to change the behavior in the hopes of getting a different result.

"I'll go to the gym three times a week!"

"I'll avoid sugar!"

"I'll plan healthy meals!"

"I'll batch cook healthy food on the weekends!"

It might work for a day, or a week, or a few weeks, but eventually we go back to our old ways and our old familiar habits. We get frustrated. We can see that our behaviors are creating our results, but we can't figure out why we can't consistently change the behavior. Well, I'm going to tell you why.

We're focused on the behavior that's getting us the result and when we fail at changing the behavior, we chalk it up to our lack of willpower or our laziness or lack of clarity around what we're supposed to be doing. But the truth is that the reason we can't change the behavior through sheer willpower alone is that the behavior has a fuel source that is incredibly powerful and it's that fuel source we need to start looking at if we want to disarm the behavior.

What is that fuel source? It's your *feelings!*

Feeling → Behavior → Result

Our behaviors are typically driven by our feelings.

We feel stressed, overwhelmed, worried, afraid, lonely, sad, angry or bored and that propels us to act in some way. Remember how we talked earlier about your brain's mission statement (avoid pain, seek pleasure and use as little energy as possible to do so)? Your brain registers those uncomfortable feelings as pain and immediately goes searching for the quickest, easiest path to pleasure (a.k.a. food).

Now, you may be saying, "Nope, I'm not feeling any particular way when I make poor food choices, I just want the food." And that's how it might appear to you on the surface, but the fact is that often what's happening is we are feeling something but we've acted in this way as a result of this feeling so many times that it's now become a habit and we're not even conscious of it anymore, however the underlying connection is still there and it's still fueling our unwanted behavior.

For example, you might describe it as simply having had a long, crazy day and craving sugar at night. But your brain is registering those feelings of stress, worry, overwhelm and fatigue as pain. Over many years it's developed a strong neural pathway around feeling those things and turning to sugar to feel better so now you do it automatically, often without even being fully aware of it, but under the surface it's still those feelings that are driving the bus.

So, our feelings are fueling our behaviors, but our feelings also have their own fuel source. Our feelings are fueled by our thoughts.

Thought → Feeling → Behavior → Result

Every feeling you have is created by a thought. You may not be conscious of the thought, but you cannot have a feeling (good or bad) without a thought. You have a thought, which creates a feeling, which triggers a behavior, which causes a result.

So, if you're feeling something unpleasant: stress, boredom, worry, loneliness, anger, frustration, and you tend to eat when you feel that feeling, we need to get curious about what the thought is that's fueling that feeling.

Because a feeling is difficult to challenge. A feeling is amorphous, it's hard to get your arms around it and really understand what's going on there, but a thought is a much clearer, often very black or white, statement. And, if you've had a thought enough times then it's often become a belief and that's something you can work with.

For example, you might be feeling stressed, but the thought fueling that feeling is likely something along the lines of: I'm afraid that something is going to fall through the cracks with this project at work and I'll be embarrassed and maybe even get fired. Or, I'm afraid that we're not going to be able to pay all these bills and we'll lose the house and be homeless. Again, you might not be going through this thought to feeling to behavior process consciously, but at the subconscious level, this is very much what's going on.

Now, if we continue peeling back these layers, what is it that's driving our thoughts? Where do our thoughts come from?

Our thoughts (especially our automatic, subconscious thoughts) are driven by our subconscious programming – I call it the "operating system" – that's working beneath the surface of your mind at all times. Your subconscious programming is a huge, complex network of neural pathways, habits and beliefs that have been formed since the day you were born. These have been created from the things you were taught as a kid, the behaviors you saw modelled around you, and the experiences you've had since then.

This subconscious programming or "operating system" is also known as your "identity." This is how you perceive the world and who you believe yourself to be in that context. It is what ultimately determines the thoughts you have, and those thoughts trigger feelings, those feelings cause behaviors and those behaviors create your results. Like this...

Identity → Thought → Feeling → Behavior → Result

So, back to where we started at the beginning of this chapter, if you're trying to be consistent with implementing new behaviors, but those new behaviors don't align with your current operating system, you won't be able to stick with them. You might be able to "white knuckle" it and force yourself to do it for a day, a few days, maybe even a week or more, but eventually you'll revert back to your old programming. I know that you've already experienced this time and time again. At this moment you're simply not the kind of person who does those things. Your subconscious programming doesn't allow it. Here's an example...

If your subconscious program says that meal planning, trying new recipes and batch cooking is very hard and unpleasant, then you're not going to do any of those things consistently, no matter how much your rational minds wants you to.

Or, if your subconscious program says that being uncomfortable (physically or emotionally) is to be avoided, then you're not going to go to the gym and push yourself regularly, and you're not going to say "no" to the cravings for sugary treats at the end of the day.

Other people have different programming. Other people's programming may tell them that planning meals and cooking is fun, or that feeling uncomfortable (physically or emotionally) is not all that bad and even often leads to big rewards. Those beliefs are literally programmed into their brains. It's part of their identity. That identity then generates different thoughts, which triggers different feelings, which result in them naturally choosing different behaviors and getting different results. It's not that they're stronger, or have more willpower, or are more committed than you but they have an internal operating system that supports those behaviors.

You might have an operating system that supports you being super organized, or a compassionate friend, or always up for an adventure. That operating system generates specific thoughts, which trigger specific feelings, which means that you choose specific behaviors, which get you specific results such as a neat home, a deep and rich social network, or the most unique and thrilling vacation experiences. Those people who easily go to the gym every night might look at you and wonder how you do it because their operating system doesn't work that way so they struggle with those things.

So, if we want to change our results, we need to move further back on the chain. We need to go all the way back to the root and focus, not on changing our behaviors, but on changing our subconscious programming, or our identity, which is ultimately driving our behaviors and determining our results. Literally changing who we are. Because that's what will ultimately change our thoughts, which will change our feelings, which will create different behaviors get us different and results.

Another way of saying this is that most people are trying to use this model:

Have → Do → Be

They say, "If I had a lean body, I would do the fitness classes at the gym, and then I would be filled with self-love and pride in myself."

This is entirely backwards. You must first be the person who would do the things that would let you have the things you want. It has to be...

Be → Do → Have

You must be the person who is filled with self-love and pride in herself, because that's the only person who will consistently do the fitness classes that will let you have the lean body you want.

The Have → Do → Be model doesn't work because you can only do the things that you would do. You can only behave in a way that aligns with your current subconscious programming. You may be able to force yourself into a behavior that doesn't align for a short time, but it will be a constant uphill battle and it won't last. The only way to make new behaviors stick long-term so that you can truly get different results is to change your subconscious programming so that it supports those new behaviors.

You have to become the person who does those things. You have to literally change who you are.

We're focused on the DO when we need to be focused on the BE. Focus on identity, not just behavior. I used the analogy earlier of trying to play a DVD in a VHS player. There's nothing wrong with the DVD, but if you keep trying to force it into the old VHS player, it's never going to work. You must first update your system to a DVD system and then the DVD will play beautifully.

So, the million-dollar question is obviously, can we do that? Can we update our operating system and change our identity? Can we become the kind of person who naturally and consistently does the things we want to do? And, if we can, *how* do we do it?

The answer is yes, you absolutely can change your subconscious programming. You can become the person who does the things you want to do. But that has to become your new focus. Not the food. Not the lack of results. Not on trying harder to stick with it. But on changing that old identity that's holding you back and keeping you stuck. When you start to change your old operating system, you're going to find yourself having new thoughts, which will trigger different feelings, which will lead to new behaviors and ultimately better results.

Okay, so how do we change our subconscious programming? How do we become the person who does the things we want to do? There are probably many ways, but I want to share five of them with you:

1. Meditation

As we saw in the last chapter, meditation shifts you into the role of the Observer. It allows you to see yourself thinking – something we rarely do. You begin to see that you are not your thoughts and that your thoughts are actually things that you can choose and change. This is an incredibly empowering thing to realize! It means that, if you want to, you can choose entirely new thoughts and beliefs. You can choose to perceive every situation in your life differently. It's not easy, but it is possible.

Also, when you meditate regularly, you start to see patterns in the themes that come up around your worries, stresses, beliefs and negative thought loops. You can begin to see where your subconscious programming is currently keeping you stuck, and you'll be in a better position to start using some of the other tools I'm going to share with you to start actively changing that. You can't change what you can't see.

2. Visualization

There's a reason why so many Olympic athletes, Fortune 500 CEOs and Academy Award winning actors credit much of their success to the practice of visualization. Visualization is simply the practice of spending time regularly imagining ourselves as already being the person we want to be. And this can't just be sticky notes on the bathroom mirror. This must be vividly felt and experienced in your mind.

Even if it looks very different than your current life, visualization works if we can bring ourselves into the feeling connected to the end result of what we want to achieve. Ask yourself, "How do I want to feel?" and then imagine yourself already feeling that way. Imagine yourself as the person you want to become in regards to your relationship with food. What does she do? How does she feel in the situations that currently trigger you? What choices does she make? How does it feel to be her?

Do this every day for a few minutes without any thought given to how you would get there. Just allow yourself to play in Imagination Land where you've already succeeded at all of it. What does that success look like in your life? How does it feel to be there? Your conscious mind (left brain) speaks with words and numbers and logic, but your subconscious mind (right brain) speaks with feelings. It's your subconscious mind you want to access and change here so you must tap into those desired feelings.

3. Change Your Environment

You've probably heard the saying that you are the average of the five people you spend the most time with. If you want to be a different person, you need to change your environment. Seek out people, places and experiences that align with the person you want to be. This doesn't mean that you need to abandon your family and move to Tibet or Bali. But start to actively seek out events, retreats, podcasts, books, groups, individuals, etc. that support the new identity you're trying to create. Make spending time absorbing this new knowledge and way of thinking, a part of your regular day.

4. Challenge Your Thoughts and be Willing to be Wrong

Your subconscious programming (your identity) creates your thoughts, but it's important to understand that your thoughts reinforce your identity.

Your brain likes to be right so when your old operating system believes something to be true, your brain then goes around seeking out evidence to support that belief and ignores any evidence that would contradict it. This reinforces the original belief and so on and so on. It becomes a self-fulfilling prophecy. You only believe what you see, but you only see what you believe.

So, become diligent about noticing your repetitive thoughts, negative thought loops, limiting beliefs, and any other thoughts flowing from that old operating system that are keeping you stuck and sabotaging your progress. These tend to work hand-in-hand with the force known as Resistance that we learned about earlier and might sound like:

"I don't have time."

"I'm not doing it right."

"It's too complicated."

"I'm not the kind of person who does that."

"That's hard for me."

"I'll probably never lose the weight."

"I don't like that."

"My husband and/or kids won't eat healthy meals."

These are all examples of old, limiting beliefs and self-sabotaging thoughts that are flowing from an old operating system. They feel like truth. They feel real. You see lots of evidence to support them. But they're just old thoughts that are creating old feelings which are triggering old behaviors and getting you the same old results.

It order to reprogram our operating system, we need to start noticing these thoughts and deliberately choosing better, more empowering thoughts and energizing those thoughts instead. This requires us to do something that we don't generally like to do, we need to be willing to be wrong about the old thoughts that we have believed for so long. We need to be willing to consider that maybe we do have the time, maybe we are doing it right, maybe it's not too complicated, maybe we are the kind of person who does these things, maybe it's not hard for us, maybe we will lose the weight, maybe we do like that and maybe our partner or kids will love healthy meals.

Holding onto those old thoughts, being "right" about them, only means that we get to keep the feelings, behaviors and results that follow. I don't know about you, but that's a prize I can do without.

As often as you can, notice when you're falling back into old thought habits or old belief structures (i.e., this is hard, I hate this, this is never going to work, I don't want to do this, I don't have time, etc.) and deliberately choose a different, more empowering thought (i.e., this is interesting, I can do hard things, I can figure this out, I know more than I sometimes give myself credit for, I'm proud of myself for doing this, this is important and worth my time, etc.).

It will be hard at first, but over time, those old thoughts will get weaker and weaker, new thoughts will lodge themselves into your operating system and your identity will change as a result.

5. Repetition

Remember what we learned earlier about how new neural pathways are formed by repetition (beating down that new path through that grassy field)? Your brain doesn't create new wiring around a thought or behavior you have or do once. You must repeat it over and over and over again in order for those neurons to fire together enough that they will eventually wire together.

Whether it's meditation, visualization or deliberately choosing more empowering thoughts, we start reprogramming our subconscious operating system by repeating these things again and again, just as you would when learning any new skill or building a new muscle -

practice, practice, practice.

The key here is to recognize and accept that, as you build these new neural pathways that will eventually form the foundation of your new identity, it will feel hard and awkward and tiring (that's old neural pathways breaking apart and new neural pathways forming). Don't give up! It will get easier.

Visualization

Most people think that they need to focus on changing their patterns and habits around food, and then they'll get the relationship with food they want. But, as we've just explored, they have it all backwards. That's the old Have - Do - Be model. The truth is, you need to focus on the relationship with food you that you want, and that's when you'll find yourself naturally gravitating to the patterns and habits around food that match it (Be - Do - Have).

But what is it that we want? You might think this sounds like the easiest question I've asked so far, but are you sure you know the answer? What does that healthy, balanced, easy relationship with food that you want so badly really look like? Who is that woman - that future you - who's living that life? What is a day in her life like? Many of us haven't spent nearly enough time examining these questions. But now that we can see that we have the power to create a new identity for ourselves around our relationship with food, these questions become among the most important ones for us to answer and where we need to start putting most of our energy and focus. If we can create what we want, what do we want to create?

What I've found is that, when it comes to food and diet and our bodies and our health, we spend an awful lot of time thinking and talking about what we don't want:

We don't want to weigh this much.

We don't want to feel tired all the time.

We don't want to feel powerless around certain foods.

We don't want it all to be so hard.

But we spend very little time thinking about what we do want.

Now, you may think you already spend lots of time thinking about what you want – too much time, in fact, but don't confuse obsessing about food with thinking about what you want; they're very different.

The problem with spending all your time focusing on where you don't want to be is that it's very hard to get somewhere if you don't know where you're going. If you got in your car with no clear destination in mind, you'd just drive around and around forever. Simply knowing that you don't want to be here is not enough.

You need to know more than just what you don't want – you need to very clearly know what you do want. What do you really want? How do you really want to feel?

It's important to know this, not just so you can set clear goals, but because the brain's power of visualization is amazing!

A little secret about your brain

Your big, beautiful brain is good at a whole lot of things, but there are a few things that it's not very good at and one of those is **knowing the difference between what's really going on and what you simply believe or imagine.** This is something that your brain really struggles with. Let me give you some examples of this in action:

This is what's going on when we talk about the "placebo effect." In a drug trial for instance, subjects are divided into two groups. One group is given simple sugar pills and the other is given the real drug and neither group knows what they got. Very often researchers see the same (sometimes even greater) improvement in the placebo group than in the group getting the real drug.

This is also what was going on in a study that was done in Toronto in which scientists split university students into two groups and had one group practice a particular piece of music on the piano every day for an hour and the other group sit and *think* about playing that same piece of music on the piano for an hour every day. They ran this experiment for about 30 days and what they found was that brain matter actually enlarged and enriched the exact same amount from both practicing the piano and *thinking* about practicing the piano.

This has even happened to you if you've ever watched a scary movie. You're watching pictures on a screen, but in the most frightening parts, your brain will begin to trigger a very real physiological fear response in the body including racing heart rate, elevated blood pressure, sweating - you might literally be on the edge of your seat. You know you're safely curled up on your couch, but your brain is easily confused between what is real and what it's merely imagining or visualizing with the help of the movie.

In fact, this goes one step further. Your brain doesn't just *react* to external factors that it imagines are real, it actually goes even one step further and *creates* what it believes to be true.

In those drug trials for example, many of the people in the placebo groups *believe* they're the ones getting the real drug so their brains take over and actually change in response – healing their bodies. In drug trials with placebo groups, we don't just see perceived improvement in symptoms, we actually see *physical* changes. These people don't just imagine that they're feeling better or in less pain, they're bodies actually begin to heal. They create what they believe to be true.

In the piano practicing study, the brains of the people who were only imagining practicing believed it was true so their brain matter changed. They actually grew new neural pathways around that new skill and became better at playing the piano as a result. They created what they believed to be true.

This is also why people who believe that the world is a horrible place and everyone is out to get them (we all know one or two of those people) tend to create that experience for themselves. They seek out evidence to support it and are blind to evidence that would contradict it. They begin to act as if it's true (being suspicious of everyone, not letting anyone get close to them, etc.) which only gives them more evidence and causes their brains to be even more convinced that what they believe is actually true. They believe the world is a horrible place so they start creating that real experience for themselves.

However, the reverse also holds true. Those people who believe that the world is mostly made up of good people who are willing and happy to help – they tend to seek out evidence to support that belief and act as if it's true (being nice to people, listening to them, having compassion) which only gives them more evidence and causes their brains to be even more convinced. They believe the world is a good place so, for them, it is.

Our brains create an experience for us that matches what we believe to be already true. In fact, so much of what we do and become and accomplish in our lives is merely a matter of how much we believe is possible. I want to share with you a little story that I think illustrates this perfectly.

For hundreds of years experts said that the human body was not capable of running a mile in under four minutes. It wasn't just dangerous they argued; it was impossible. And for all those hundreds of years, no one did it. Professional runners, Olympians – no one believed it was possible (the experts said it wasn't) so that's the reality that they created and no one was ever able to do it.

Then, on May 6, 1954, Roger Bannister broke the four minute barrier, running the distance in 3:59. Bannister said in interviews afterwards that he spent far more time visualizing himself breaking the record than physically training for the run. Once he could see it clearly in his mind, believed it was possible, and practiced seeing himself doing it over and over again, he was able to achieve it. Bannister's accomplishment alone illustrates my point. By working on visualizing it happening – seeing it as true – he was able to create that reality.

However, what's even more amazing is that, Bannister's new world record lasted for only a few months. Almost immediately after Bannister broke this record that had stood for centuries, hundreds of other people began running sub-four minutes miles. As soon as they saw Bannister do it, they believed it was possible and could visualize it happening so they did it. Nothing about the human body had changed. Nothing about physics had changed. The only thing that had changed was their belief. If you can visualize it and if you can believe that it's possible, then it often is.

Okay, but what does all this have to do with changing our relationship with food?

Well, think back to what we talked about earlier now that you know this interesting secret about your brain. If you're spending all your time focusing your attention on believing that this is all too hard, too complicated and that you'll never lose the weight, and if your brain can't tell the difference between what's real and what you're just imagining and will actually start to create more of whatever it is that you believe, well, can you see where this is going?

But, the good news is that now that we understand this, we can start harnessing this power for our benefit. If you can start deliberately and intentionally moving your attention away from what you don't want and towards a clear and compelling vision of what you do want, and if you do this deliberately and regularly (daily), then the same phenomena will result in your brain assuming that *that* is real and it will start naturally gravitating towards the healthy choices that match it.

Pretty exciting, right? But, before you run off trying to trick your brain into craving kale, there's a few things you need to understand about how this process of visualization works and how you can start using it yourself.

There's one thing that the people in the placebo groups of drug trials, or the students in the piano practicing study, or Roger Bannister, or you when you watched that scary movie all had in common – you all had a *clear* and *vivid* vision in your mind of what you were imagining. Because the truth is that **your brain will only be tricked into adopting a vision as reality if the vision is crystal clear and incredibly vivid.**

The people taking the placebo pill know *exactly* how they want this drug to make them feel (free from life-long pain or crippling depression, etc.). They know exactly what that pain or depression-free life would look like because they've probably fantasized about it every day for years.

The piano practicers focused very clearly on the *exact* key strokes of that specific piece of music over and over again.

Roger Bannister visualized the time clock at the finish line with a big flashing "3" in front of it. He could feel the sun on his face, hear the crowd in the stands, he could smell the asphalt track under his shoes. He knew exactly how the whole race would look and feel.

And, when you're sitting in that movie theatre, you're not watching a white screen with stick figures stabbing one another. No, there's lighting, costumes, make-up, music and camera angles that all work together to create this clear and vivid experience that feels terrifying.

So, it follows that if you want your brain to adopt a new relationship with food, it needs to know exactly what that looks like, feels like, sounds like and tastes like. It's by clearly knowing what you want and practicing feeling it that you'll actually start to create it in your experience.

Having a clear and compelling vision for what you want is important because it's the only way that your brain will follow your thoughts and create that as your reality. If your brain can see it clearly and vividly, it will begin to create new neural pathways around that vision and the habits that will most closely align with it.

But there's another reason why having a clear and compelling vision around the relationship that you want to have with food is important, and that is that it serves as an incredibly helpful tool when temptation strikes and things get tough. Because things will get tough. Your gorgeous, juicy vision gives you something to turn to when you do feel tempted to fall into old, unhelpful habits around food.

Let me explain. If the choice is just, have a delicious cookie or don't have a delicious cookie because you probably shouldn't – guess which one wins? But if the choice is have a delicious cookie, or make a healthier choice that brings you more into alignment with your vision of a vibrant, energized, happy, confident, relaxed, strong and sexy you – suddenly the cookie doesn't always win. Suddenly you've stacked the deck a little bit in your favour. If your vision is way better than the cookie, then it becomes a little easier to say no to the cookie.

Okay, so I hope you can see why having a specific, vivid and compelling vision for how you want your relationship with food to look is so important. Now, how do you go about creating that vision for yourself?

Creating your Vision

This is the fun part, but it's also important that you follow a few key guidelines as you embark on this.

First, when you set about creating your vision of what you want, things like, "Have lots of energy," "Crave healthy food," and "Stay at my goal weight" are not going to cut it. These are not *clear*. They're vague and will not trick your brain into believing they're already real.

The other problem with a vision like "lose weight" or "have more energy" is that it's not *vivid* enough to trick your brain into believing that this is already happening. No new neural pathways are going to be wired together.

Roger Bannister didn't visualize himself "running really fast," he specifically worked on seeing himself running across that thick white finish line and seeing that big black time clock with a bright red number "3" flashing in the first block. He could hear his shoes on the track and the popcorn sellers shouting to the crowd.

Similarly, if someone describes a scary movie to you by saying, "This woman goes for a walk in the forest and gets murdered," you're probably not going to feel your heart rate speed up or have the urge to jump out of your skin.

This vision that you're going to create needs be just as clear and vivid as that scary movie you watched in the theatre that had you tossing your popcorn and sleeping with the light on for a week. Think of it like your own personal movie that you're designing and directing in your head.

How to Start

A good way to start to create your amazingly clear and vivid vision is to simply list words that describe how you want to *feel*. Imagine yourself a year from now. Imagine that you've achieved all the goals that you currently have for your body and your health. How does that future you feel? Some examples might be: vibrant, sexy, confident, grounded, light, powerful, strong, happy, relaxed or energized. Take some time with this and list as many as you can that feel really good to you.

Next, I want you to build on those words and start thinking about some of the actual activities, routines or rituals that you would like to be part of your regular life that would illicit some of those desired feelings that you identified with your words. What kinds of things could the future you be doing on a daily or weekly basis that would help create those feelings you identified earlier (e.g., yoga, painting, laughing, reading, cooking, learning, meditation, writing, teaching, dancing, napping, volunteering, etc.)?

And finally, you continue to build on that by creating a complete movie in your mind around your perfect day. Imagine that you're a year in the future. You did all the things you were supposed to do. You checked all the boxes and have reached all your goals. You did it. What does your life look like now? What would a typical day in that life of the future you look like? Here are a few questions to help you begin to craft this vision. Remember to answer these as the future you who already has everything that you currently desire:

Where do you wake up?

Who do you wake up next to?

Where in the world are you?

What is the first thought that enters your mind when you open your eyes?

What is your intention for this day?

What does your morning routine look like?

What do you eat for breakfast? Where do you eat?

117

How do you spend the first few hours of your day?

What words best describe the way you feel during this time?

What do you eat for lunch? Where do you eat?

What do you do in the afternoon?

Who are the people closest to you and what does your time with them look and feel like?

How did you move your body today?

What projects are you currently working on?

How did you feed your soul today?

What do you eat for dinner? Where do you eat?

How do you start winding down in the evening?

What part of your day do you enjoy most?

What are your last thoughts before bed?

What are you grateful for?

What are you most proud of in your life right now?

What are you looking forward to?

There is just one important rule with this exercise: You must be guided by only what you *want*. You cannot write down things that you believe you *should* want. These scenes or scenarios need to feel amazing and compelling for you. They need to be what you want more than anything. So, if doing yoga sounds awful to you, don't put it in your vision!

Now, before you go off creating your own vision, one word of caution (not a rule, but a suggestion). Don't get caught in the trap of creating a vision that sounds like "I eat French fries all day and never gain a pound." Or "I sit on the couch all day and still look like a supermodel."

These are tempting visions – I get it. But if you're honest with yourself I think you'll see that they are just a reaction to years of feeling deprived. I encourage you to think bigger for yourself. Don't make the highest vision of your life be you sitting on the couch eating French Fries. Think bigger.

Now, once you have created your clear and vivid vision, you don't just close your journal and put it back on the shelf, you have to use it, work with it, practice it.

Visualization Practice

Just so you know, you already have a daily visualization practice, you just might not be aware of it. You already wake up every morning and immediately start imagining how things are going to go for you. That's what you believe, so that's generally what ends up happening. Perhaps you imagine yourself stressed, overwhelmed and tired and then it's no coincidence that that's what you end up experiencing during your day.

What I'm asking you to do is to start using that superpower you already have and use every day, but point it towards a more positive and empowering target.

In order to make your new visualization practice work best I encourage you to do it every day. This creates the greatest impact but also helps it become a habit. This doesn't have to take a long time. You need only spend 3-5 minutes a day doing this. And you can do this anywhere. Do it in the shower, immediately following your daily meditation, while you're walking the dog or waiting in line for coffee.

For those 3-5 minutes, go into your vision and really imagine yourself in it. This is nothing more complicated than basic imagination. It's something you likely did as a kid all the time. Imagine yourself already having it all and walking around it. See yourself in that perfect day you created earlier. Imagine yourself living that life. Let all the amazing, exciting, happy feelings that come from seeing yourself like that wash over you. Marinate in those feelings until you almost can't help but smile as you're thinking about how good it feels.

Once your brain can clearly see and feel it as real on a regular basis, it will begin to believe that you already are that person and start to naturally pull you towards the choices and actions that best match it.

You can also pull your vision out of your toolbox when you find yourself feeling tempted by something that you know isn't going to serve you. Take a moment to breathe, feel strong and grounded and conjure up that vision in your mind. Really see and feel yourself being it and having it. Think about what that woman would do in this situation. What choice would she make? How would she feel? Think about how empowering it will feel to make a choice that brings you more into alignment with that amazing vision of your future self.

If you struggle to create your vision from scratch, another way you can approach this is by taking a challenging situation that you already often find yourself in from time to time and re-writing it the way you would like for it to go.

Re-Writing

Think about a situation that you regularly find yourself in where you're frustrated by the choices you typically end up making. Maybe it's a regular evening at home when you end up sabotaging the good choices you made all day by bingeing on ice cream while in front of the TV. Maybe it's a social situation like dinner out at a restaurant or a family birthday party where you end up eating way too much of the wrong things because you get caught up in the fun. Maybe it's simply a busy afternoon at work where you find yourself going for the chocolate bar because you're tired and stressed. Once you've picked your scenario, you're going to re-write it exactly the way you would *want* it to look and feel.

For example, imagine yourself at that birthday party. You walk into the room feeling totally confident, relaxed and thrilled with the way you look and the way you carry yourself. People notice you when you come into that room. There is food everywhere, but you barely even notice. It has no power over you. You spend your time talking to the people you care about. You laugh, you catch up, you really connect. You feel relaxed, confident and totally at ease. A little later you wander over to the food table and choose a few of the foods you enjoy for your plate. You sit and eat them slowly, feeling no urge to over-do it. You get a clear signal from your body when you're satisfied and you end up even leaving a few things on your plate since you've had enough. There's no agonizing about it; you don't even want anything else. You leave the party later feeling like you had a wonderful time and proud of the choices you made, knowing that you were in total control and honoured what your body needed.

The Horrible Hows

One important thing to remember when you're creating your vision is not to get caught up in the *how*. Don't worry about how you would get from where you are now to that amazing future you. The how is none of your concern during this process. For our purposes here, we're just going to assume that you did whatever needed to be done to get from here to there. Just enjoy how amazing it feels to imagine yourself already being there.

Talisman

Another great way to put your new vision and visualization practice to work for you is to use it in conjunction with a talisman.

The dictionary describes a "talisman" as, "Anything whose presence exercises a remarkable or powerful influence on human feelings or actions." Talismans are essentially objects that we give meaning to and they have been used throughout human history. Think of the ring in the *Lord of the Rings*, the Holy Grail of so many Arthurian legends, or the diamond necklace in the movie, Titanic. Wedding bands, antiques and keepsakes from loved ones who have passed on are all forms of talismans. A talisman holds meaning for us, and when we carry it, touch it or look at it, we're instantly reminded of that meaning.

From a neurological perspective, the talisman serves as a cue, which triggers a thought, memory or feeling. In this case, your clear and compelling vision of your future self. Here's how you can put a talisman to work for you:

First, select your talisman. Anything can be turned into a talisman, but something like a piece of jewelry, a watch, or a small rock or crystal works best because you can easily carry it with you pretty much anywhere you go (without looking too weird).

Next, "load" it with your intention by sitting with it for a few minutes, closing your eyes and focusing on your vision – particularly on how you will feel when you have the healthy life you dream of. Once you have that image in your mind, look closely at your talisman, turn it around in your fingers, make the connection in your mind between that feeling and your talisman.

Finally, carry it with you. Every time you feel tempted to make a choice that doesn't serve your highest good, touch it and remember your vision. Remember that feeling wonderful of success.

A talisman is a great tool to take with you into social situations (parties, restaurants, etc.) or when you're traveling and are worried about making healthy choices. Load your talisman before you go, take it with you and use it every time you feel tempted.

Create an Alter Ego

In Todd Herman's excellent book, *The Alter Ego Effect*, he talks about the power of creating an alter ego for yourself in certain areas of your life where you're not performing your best.

Herman works mostly with high performance athletes and entrepreneurs, but I believe that this tool can be just as effective for those struggling to be more consistent with healthy choices. I also think that Herman's work in this area ties really beautifully into what we're talking about here in terms of creating a vision for the kind of healthy, strong, confident, fulfilled person you want to become.

Herman suggests that we identify a specific area of our lives that we want to improve in and create an alter ego for ourselves in that area. So, for our purposes here you'll want to create an alter ego who will help you when you're making choices about food or your health in general. You can think about people that you either know personally, people you have been around (maybe someone in your yoga class), or even famous people living or dead and pulling together the qualities that you most admire in them into one super alter ego for yourself.

He suggests that you give your alter ego a name and choose some kind of object that you can use to flip the switch when you need to turn your alter ego on, just like Superman uses a pair of glasses to shift into mild mannered reporter Clark Kent.

Start thinking about what kind of alter ego you might want to create for yourself around this area of eating right and making healthy choices. Who can you draw from to create her? What is her name? What kind of totem or talisman can you use to help call her up when you need her most?

PILLAR TWO: Know Where You're Going
TRY THIS

Identity → Thought → Feeling → Behavior → Result - Instead of just focusing on how your behaviors create your results, go deeper. Start noticing how your behaviors are determined by your feelings, your feelings are triggered by your thoughts and your thoughts are flowing from your identity.

Be → Do → Have instead of Have → Do → Be – Shift your focus from what you want to have to who you need to be.

Experiment with transforming your old identity starting with these five tools:

- *Meditation* – A daily practice will help you begin to see patterns and themes in the negative and limiting thoughts you have on a daily basis that are keeping you stuck.

- *Visualization* – Spend a few minutes every day imagining yourself as the person you want to be until you can really feel how it feels to be her.

- *Change your environment* – Expose yourself to new ideas and other people who are doing the same work. Attend retreats and conferences, listen to podcasts, read books and join groups online and in person.

- *Challenge your thoughts and be willing to be wrong* – If you want to be right about your old, limiting thoughts then all you get to do is keep them.

- *Repetition* – Make this work an ongoing project. This will get easier, but it takes time.

Create your vision - Start with a list of words that light you up. Next brainstorm some of the activities, rituals or routines that you would enjoy doing that would make up a life built on those words. Finally, imagine that it's a year from now and you're exactly where you want to be, imagine what that life looks like for the future you. Picture her typical day. Make it as clear and vivid as you possibly can. How does it feel?

Re-Write – If you struggle to create a vision from scratch, start by taking a situation that you currently regularly find yourself in where you're frustrated by the choices you typically end up making. Re-write this situation in your mind the way that you would love for it to go. This can be your clear and vivid vision to start.

Start a daily visualization practice - Just 3-5 minutes a day. Do it anywhere you can let your mind wander into imaginary land. See your future self living that amazing day or see that previously challenging situation re-written the way you'd like it to go. Feel how good it feels. Let those wonderful feelings seep into every cell in your body until it feels like it's already real. Do this every day.

Try using a talisman - Choose a small object or piece of jewelry that you can carry with you. Hold it while you do your visualization. Take it with you into challenging situations and every time you touch it you'll be instantly reminded of that clear, vivid and incredible vision you have for yourself.

Try creating an alter ego - Think of your future self as an alter ego that you can step into any time you need to tap into her strength - like Superman for Clark Kent. Give her a name.

Consider using your talisman as a way to help you flip into being her when you need to. Call on her when you find yourself in a challenging situation. What would she do? How would she feel? What would she think? How would she react?

Chapter 9

PILLAR THREE: Feel the Feelings

Each of the five pillars are important, but this one (if you can really master it) is the most like a superpower. That's because, if you can get to a place where you can feel your feelings, including cravings, without rushing to food to avoid them or push them away, you will finally be free of your battle with food. You will be able to make choices about what you eat and how much based entirely on what your body needs rather than on how you're feeling. Think about it...

Imagine if you could simply allow feelings such as stress, anxiety or boredom without using food to manage them?

Imagine if you could sit with the intense, hot urge of a craving without letting it tell you what to do?

Imagine if you could enjoy the taste of a few bites of your favourite food and then allow the dopamine receptors in your brain to scream at you to have more, without giving in to them?

The truth is that almost all of our negative choices and patterns around food stem from a desire to avoid uncomfortable feelings. When we're craving something, or when we feel tired, stressed, bored, lonely, overwhelmed, resentful, unappreciated or unfulfilled – we look to food to numb or avoid those feelings. Because these feelings don't feel good! To your brain, they feel like pain. And remember what we learned about how your brain measures every choice it makes against its single mission statement: avoid pain and seek pleasure in the most efficient way possible.

We binge on junk food at the end of a long day because we're exhausted, overwhelmed and often feeling unappreciated and unfulfilled. It doesn't feel good. But we know that potato chips and

126

ice cream feel good! So guess what we do? We're not weak or lazy. We repeat this pattern because it works! It protects us from having to sit with feelings that scare us; feelings that feel too big and too difficult. It allows us to move quickly and efficiently from pain to pleasure. Your brain is doing exactly what it's designed to do.

It's the same with cravings. We give in to cravings because they don't feel good. They feel like something bigger and more powerful than we believe we can handle. We don't want to feel the craving so we eat the food to make it go away. But, what if you could crave something and just allow yourself to experience that craving without acting on it? What if the feeling could just be felt and, by being felt, lose all its power?

If you can get to a place where you can just sit with your feelings and feel them without trying to run away, you will truly be free from your struggle with food.

And I don't mean get over your feelings or distract yourself from them; I mean sit with them. I mean, identify what you're feeling (e.g., "I'm feeling overwhelmed by life right now and afraid that I'm going to fail") and let it come. Feelings are just energy. They can't hurt you. If you let them come and flow through you without resisting them, then you can let them go.

This food-feeling connection is tricky, not only because your brain is hard-wired to avoid pain and seek pleasure, but also because for most of us, using food to avoid feelings is a habit now. It's moved into our subconscious. We feel a certain way and then we want a certain food and we don't really question why. We chalk it up to "cravings" or "a sweet tooth," but in order to break the habit, we need to pull ourselves out of that auto-pilot state, get much more curious about the feelings that are driving our food choices and be ready to feel those feelings instead of using food to numb or avoid them.

Feelings are our friends

Feelings are not the enemy. In fact, feelings are important sources of information. Every feeling has a message for us. Sometimes we don't want to hear that message but the feeling likely won't go away until you receive and accept its message. If a feeling persists, ask it what it wants to tell you. Sit quietly and allow the answer to appear. Be open to receiving the answer, whether or not you like what that answer is or have a solution for it in this moment. You can feel a feeling like anger, worry, loneliness or overwhelm without having to know how you'll fix it.

We have to feel our feelings because it's the only way for them to move on. You may have heard the saying that, "The only way out is through." Avoiding feelings actually makes them stronger and gives them more power over us. The avoidance of suffering is a form a suffering. The avoidance of struggle *is* a struggle. Avoiding your feelings isn't bringing you peace, it's causing you more pain.

An emotion swept under the rug is not an emotion that goes away; it's simply an emotion that is put somewhere other than where it should be put. It becomes inert rather than dynamic energy, stored within you rather than being released.

Actually, an emotion is not dangerous *until* it's ignored because that's when it usually gets projected onto others or twisted and turned on ourselves as self-judgement and self-hatred. That only produces more negative feelings—shame, humiliation, embarrassment, and failure—resulting in an endless barrage of reasons we give ourselves for why we're always going to fail and might as well just give up and eat more now.

It's not about pretending problems and challenges don't exist or trying to distract ourselves from them. It's about addressing the feelings they're creating head on, welcoming them, being curious about them, seeing what they have to teach us, thanking them for showing up to get our attention and pointing us in the direction we need to look.

Where feelings come from

So, we can see how important it is that we feel the feelings and stop trying to avoid or numb them with food, but where do these feelings come from? As we learned earlier, every feeling comes from a thought. You can't have a feeling (good or bad) without a thought. A thought creates a feeling, which triggers a behavior. You think you're going to fail at all the things you've got going on at work and be embarrassed in front of your boss and co-workers; that makes you feel stressed, overwhelmed, afraid; and that makes you reach for certain foods to make those feelings go away.

If you're feeling something strong (good or bad), it's because of a thought you're having and the only way to start to tackle the feeling, is to first identify the thought creating it. A question that I love to stop and ask myself whenever I find myself feeling particularly triggered by something is, "What am I making this mean?" The situation is never the problem, it's always the thought you're having about it or the meaning that you're giving to that situation that is creating those feelings in you.

The brilliant researcher and writer, Brené Brown, says that the words she uses when she's investigating her own feelings and attempting to understand the thoughts behind them is, "The story I'm telling myself here is…"

For example, if I'm feeling stressed and worried about one of my kids struggling at school, the story I'm telling myself or the thought I'm believing is that if my kids struggle it means I'm not doing a good job as a mother. It's that thought, belief or story that "if my kids struggle it means I'm not doing a good job as a mother," that is creating the feeling of stress. Once you've identified that thought, you can begin to get curious about it and challenge it. Is it true? Might something else be at least equally true? How do I feel when I believe this? How would things be different if I didn't believe this?

Okay, so we see that our thoughts are creating our feelings and it's very often the desire (conscious or unconscious) to make those feelings go away that drives us towards making not-so-great food choices. But life is going to keep happening around us. We're going to feel stressed and anxious and bored from time to time. So, what can we do when we find ourselves caught up in those feelings and craving food as a way to change the way we feel?

How to Feel the Feelings (instead of eating them)

I'm sure you can see how this work requires us to become much more conscious and aware of the thoughts and feelings that are driving our behaviors around food. This means that the first step in feeling the feelings is to get out of auto-pilot (see Pillar One) and come into the present moment since you cannot observe your thoughts or feelings when you're in auto-pilot.

When you can feel yourself on the precipice of making a not-so-healthy food choice, stop yourself for one second and take three deep breaths. You can do this anywhere and at any time, no matter who's around. Do this as you sit down to the big holiday dinner with family. Do it while you're reading the menu at the restaurant. Do it as you're sitting on the couch thinking about the potato chips in the kitchen pantry. Step number one is always to stop, breathe and come into the present moment.

Brain dump

If you have more time, a great exercise to try after you take those three deep breaths is a simple brain dump. Often we've got so much going on up there that we struggle to know where to begin in examining it all. A great way to gain some clarity is to get it out of your head and get it down onto a piece of paper where you can take a closer look at it.

You can do this by sitting down with a pen and a journal or even a blank document on your computer and simply starting to write down everything that's going on in your head, stream of consciousness-style. Write down everything you're thinking and worrying about. Big things, small things, serious things and ridiculous things - get as much of it down as quickly as you can.

This doesn't need to make any sense at all. In fact, you'll really know you're doing this right when you pick up your pen after writing for a few minutes and realize that what you've written sounds like the ramblings of a mad man.

It might sound something like this: Make vet appt, how much? Roof fixed? How much? Birthday party at Susan's - need to get a gift. Chicken for dinner? Cook the asparagus before it goes bad. Eat more veggies. Susan - candle? Book? Scarf? Re-gift? Do tax stuff this weekend. Weeding. Wash bedding...

This exercise is useful for a few reasons. First, it's going to help you start to identify the stressful thoughts that you might be using food to avoid (in the example above there might be worries about money as well as feelings of not-enoughness and overwhelm).

Second, when you do this often over time you start to notice recurring themes in the things you think and worry about. This is enormously helpful because you can't change what you're not aware of, but once you start to see the thought habit loops that your brain is repeating again and again (your "Top 10 Greatest Hits"), you can start to catch yourself in those loops and consciously choose better feeling thoughts to break those old thought habits.

NAIL

As I mentioned earlier, this isn't about "getting over" your feelings or distracting yourself from them. Feelings are important messengers and we want to work *with* them instead of avoiding or ignoring them. But this also isn't just about wallowing in pain or (worse) self-pity. Instead, our intention here should be to feel the feelings so that we can process through them.

So, while you're sitting with the feeling and not reaching for food, there are four steps I encourage you to take that will help you process the feelings in a healthy and positive way. I created a handy acronym to help you remember the four steps: NAIL (Name it, allow it, investigate it, and look for a slightly better thought and/or activity). Let's dive into each one a little more deeply.

Name it

As early as you can, catch yourself when you're heading into the old habit of rushing to use food to soothe an uncomfortable feeling be it an emotion or a craving. Stop, breathe and come into the present moment. Instead of mindlessly following the same old habit of having a feeling and turning to food, stop yourself and shine a light on it. Pause as you're reaching for that potato chip and get curious about what you're *really* feeling. **Give the feeling a name.** Label it. Maybe it's tired, empty, bored, lonely, anxious, angry, worried or stressed.

Sometimes we know exactly what we're feeling when we're eating. We've all had those days where we felt stressed, hurt or sad and we very consciously decided to use food to numb the feeling. For example, ice cream after a break up, a glass of wine after a stressful day, etc. We know exactly what we're doing in those moments.

However, other times it's not as easy to connect the dots. Very often when I teach this concept to my students, while they are cautiously open to the idea of feeling their feelings instead of eating them, the very first hurdle they face is in identifying what it is that they're feeling.

"I don't think I'm feeling anything," they say. "I just really want the chips."

So, it could be that the feeling you're avoiding is simply the craving itself, but it could also be that using food to avoid emotional feelings has simply become an automatic habit.

Often these neural pathways started being formed at an incredibly young age. As kids how many of us remember being given food when we were sad or hurt? You skinned your knee? Let's go get an ice cream cone. You didn't get the part in the school play? Mom's going to make you your favourite dinner to cheer you up. Our parents meant well, they just wanted to make us feel better, but unfortunately what was also happening here was that our brains were beginning to learn that when we felt something uncomfortable (physically or emotionally) we could use food to move away from that pain. Can you just hear the neural pathways being fused together there?

As we got older, we continued to use food to manage feelings on our own and now, after years and even decades of repetition, these neural pathways are deeply ingrained so that we now repeat these patterns, often without even being conscious of it.

When this happens and we can no longer clearly see how the dots from our feelings to our desire for food are connected, we tend to simply lump all of those desires under the umbrella of "cravings." We don't really know why we want it, we just really, really want it.

The problem here is that a feeling feels even scarier and more unmanageable when you can't identify it. The monster under the bed is always far more terrifying than anything you can see. But, when you name a feeling, give it a label and know that it's stress or worry or boredom that you're feeling, while it's still challenging to sit with, it now starts to be something that you can get curious about, work with and manage in a much more effective manner than simply trying to push it away with food.

So, as I mentioned, very often when I ask people what feeling they're using the food to avoid, they respond with, "I have no idea. It just tastes good."

That's a great place to start, but the truth is that lots of things taste good. Peaches, blueberries, walnuts and cinnamon all taste wonderful. But we don't tend to feel as overwhelmed by cravings for them as we do for our potato chips, ice cream and chocolate. And yes, certainly those foods offer quick jolts of sugar to the body which spikes dopamine in the brain, but so would eating plain white sugar but nobody's sitting in front of the TV with a bowl of sugar cubes.

The truth is that there's something deeper going on here. You wanted the ice cream or the potato chips for a reason. You associate certain feelings with your "treats," feelings like calm, love, security, safety, happiness, fun and it's those feelings that you seek more than the food itself. Our end goal here is going to be to help you achieve those positive feelings in ways that don't involve food, but the first step to getting there is naming the feelings we're using the food to help us manage.

If you're still struggling to name the feeling and all you're coming up with is, "I just want it!" try asking yourself when you're deep in a craving, **"How am I hoping this food will make me *feel*?"** Because whatever the answer to that question is it will usually be the exact *opposite* of the uncomfortable feeling you're trying to use food to avoid.

For example, maybe you're hoping the food will make you feel nurtured, loved, complete, treasured, full or satisfied. Often we say, "I feel like I just need a little something," or "I deserve a treat after the day I've had!" These are perfect examples of us attempting to use food to avoid feeling overwhelmed, depleted and unappreciated. Spoiler alert: food can't do any of those things for you.

Another trick if you're having a hard time with this is to try imagining that it would be absolutely impossible for you to have the food you crave. Imagine that it's a holiday or something and you have none of that food in your house and every store is closed. It's absolutely impossible for you to get that food. See what your brain's response is to that message. Sometimes doing this imagination exercise will trigger your brain into throwing a little temper tantrum and through that tantrum it will reveal how it was hoping that food was going to make it feel.

Allow it

Next, once we've named the feeling for what it truly is, we allow it. Now, "allow" has two meanings here:

First, we allow it by just letting it in. When I think of this I like to imagine my smelly wet dog out in the rain. I don't really want him in the house, but I don't have much choice. I have to let him in – stinky, muddy puddle water and all. It's not that I'm thrilled about it. It's not that I want to invite *more* stinky wet dogs in, but I do need to stop trying to press the door shut, relax and let him come in.

Simply allow that this is how you're feeling right now: You're stressed, you're worried, you're bored, you're lonely, you're hurt, you're craving sugar. Whatever it is that you're feeling, just allow that feeling to be there. See it. Sit with it. Like having a cold. It's not super pleasant, but you have to just allow that it's here.

This is hard because your brain's natural tendency is to bolt away from uncomfortable feelings – like pulling your hand from a hot

134

stove. But, as overwhelming as they can feel, intense feelings – bad or good – never last long. Studies have shown that the strongest part of a feeling only lasts for about 90 seconds. You can sit with a feeling and breathe through it for 90 seconds. I know you can.

Next, we allow in the sense that we accept that things are as they are. We let go of the negative meaning we've attached to whatever is happening.

The Buddha said that all of our suffering comes from our desire for things to be different than they are. Feelings such as hurt, resentment, worry, disappointment – these are all feelings associated with wishing that things were different than they are. Another way of saying this is that, when our beliefs and reality don't mesh, we suffer. So, for example, when we believe that someone should speak to us in a certain way and they don't do that, we suffer.

We're unhappy that we weigh what we weigh, because we have a belief around what we should weigh and what it means that we weigh more than that (we're weak, undisciplined, unattractive, etc.). Or, we have a belief that says, "People should be kinder" or, "My neighbors should take better care of their lawn" or, "The line at the grocery store should move faster" or, "My husband should say certain things to me" or, "I should be thinner (or prettier or more successful)." These are all ways that our beliefs argue with reality. And when we believe things that are not consistent with reality, we experience tension and frustration. When we stop opposing reality, action becomes simple, fluid and intuitive.

But, here's the thing: things cannot be different than they are. Not in this moment. It's absolutely impossible. They might be different next week, or tomorrow, or in five minutes. But right now they cannot be different than they are. And because of that, whenever we wish they were different, we suffer.

One of my favourite quotes is from Byron Katie who said: "I am a lover of what is, not because I'm a spiritual person, but because it hurts when I argue with reality." We must stop arguing with reality if we want to free ourselves from the suffering.

Now, please do not confuse accepting that things are the way they are with never trying to change – they are not the same thing. You can accept that things are as they are and, at the very same time, be actively planning to change them. Let me illustrate this with a story...

Former South African President and civil rights activist, Nelson Mandela, was imprisoned for 27 years, 18 of those on Robben Island off the coast of Cape Town, South Africa. Mandela and the other prisoners (many of whom were fellow fighters of the apartheid movement) were completely isolated, got little to eat and had to undertake the grueling work of pounding rocks into gravel.

They said later that, what kept them sane was the community they formed for themselves and remembering that they still had important work to do. Historians often refer to the prison during that time as 'Robben Island University' because Mandela and his fellow prisoners began to study everything from politics to their individual areas of expertise. Mandela also believed that he was serving a larger purpose in jail and didn't hold it against his guards. That lack of personal animosity toward those in charge of his confinement was vitally important to his mental health and survival.

Mandela could have chosen to argue with reality. He could have chosen to believe that it was "unfair" that he was in prison. That it was "wrong" and let his anger and resentment consume him. Instead he chose to accept what was and continue to take action towards his goals.

Acceptance doesn't mean apathy, but it does relieve anxiety.

Now, some people worry that, if they don't argue with reality, they won't be motivated to act and change things for the better. That if they don't feel the pain, they won't feel any reason to change. But, the experience of those who truly accept that things are the way they are in this moment is that the exact opposite is true.

Suffering is not required for us to move in a new direction. Suffering steals our focus and energy. It actually constricts us, hardens us and limits our ability to see options, think creatively and initiate transformation.

You can be stuck in a traffic jam, and not need to feel angry or

136

frustrated in order to start looking for an alternate route.

You can have someone yelling at you or physically hurting you, and not need to feel angry or afraid or like a victim in order to decide that this is not a person that you wish to spend any more time with.

You can feel physically uncomfortable with your weight, and not need to hate yourself or feel ashamed or inadequate in order to start creating a plan to take some of the weight off.

You can allow that the situation is what it is, without believing that it "should" be any different, and still decide that you'd prefer to move in a different direction or take steps to change the situation in some way.

Nelson Mandela accepted the reality of what was happening to him. He let go of any belief around how things "should" be. This didn't mean that he just sat in his jail cell and waited to be let out, no, he worked to further his education, he created a community with his fellow prisoners, and he planned a national revolution that changed the world and eventually resulted in his release, all from inside the prison walls. But he did it free of the hatred, resentment or anger that would have come from his focusing on believing that things should be different than they were.

So, allow your feelings. Allow them in without fear or resistance and allow that whatever is making you feel that way is as it is and that in this moment it cannot be any other way. Stop fighting with reality. You're only hurting yourself.

Investigate It

Now that you've named the feeling and allowed it, let's check this thing out a bit more, shall we? What's really going on here? Where did this feeling come from? What is the thought you believe that's fueling this feeling? What are you making this mean? What's the story that you're telling yourself here?

For example, let's say you paused on your way to the cookie jar, took a deep breath and tried to name the feeling. Maybe the name you came up with was "stressed." Next, you allowed the feeling of stress to simply be there and you also relaxed and stopped believing that you *shouldn't* feel stressed. Next, let's investigate what the *thought* is that's creating this feeling of stress.

Perhaps the thought behind your feeling is that you've got too much on your plate at work. Maybe you're afraid that you're going to drop the ball or let something fall through the cracks and appear incompetent in front of your boss and co-workers.

It's difficult to argue with a feeling like stress, but a thought like, "I'm going to fail and be humiliated," is something more concrete, more black and white, that you can work with. You can investigate a thought and ask it questions. Put it on the witness stand and demand that it defend itself and it's right to take up space in your head.

Look for a better thought or activity

So, you've named the feeling, you've allowed it to be here and you've done some investigation into where that feeling is coming from and the thought or belief that's fueling it. Now it's time to address that troublesome thought by looking either for a thought that feels better or for an activity (other than eating) that will make you feel better (or both). Remember the cue, routine, reward loop. Your brain needs that reward but let's find a better, healthier way to get there.

First, let's look at how you can create a better feeling thought. Because, when a thought or belief is creating an uncomfortable feeling that's driving you to eat, it's important to remember that you actually get to choose your thoughts. The thoughts that you're having about the events going on in your life are all a choice and you can choose ones that will feel better.

I had a profound personal experience with this several years ago. Out of the blue I received a letter from the government indicating that my husband and I owed an additional $11,000 in taxes for the previous year. I remember opening that letter and the feeling of my stomach dropping as I realized what it said. I already felt as though we were barely keeping our heads above water financially, barely able to get all the bills paid each month. We had no savings to speak of and I had absolutely no idea where this huge amount was going to come from. There was no way we could pay this.

I felt fear about what this was going to mean for our family and also embarrassment about our financial situation. The story I was telling myself was that successful adults are financially organized and never surprised or unprepared for anything.

l didn't want my kids to see how overwhelmed I was feeling so I went into the bathroom, closed the door and sank down to the floor. I cried. Long, sobbing tears. In that moment it felt like more than I could handle. What were we going to do? It felt like I'd been stressing about money on an almost daily basis since the day I'd first left home. I'd always felt stupid and ashamed when it came to money. Always felt like I was doing it wrong while everyone else had it all figured out. More than anything I was just so sick and tired of feeling like a failure and I remember sitting on that floor thinking, "I don't want to feel this way any more." And almost immediately I heard in my head a little voice that said, "So don't."

Despite having learned a great deal about our power to choose our thoughts, I'd never actually put it into practice around my struggle with money. But in that moment I realized with absolute clarity that, while I couldn't change the fact that I owed this money to the government, I could entirely change the way I thought about it and, in turn, the way it was making me feel.

I decided in that moment to simply stop feeling stressed about money. Did that mean that the bills stopped coming or that we were still often short at the end of the month? Nope. But it entirely changed the way those situations affected me. I realized that making a plan to pay off that tax bill did not require me to be stressed, worried, afraid, or ashamed. In fact none of those thoughts or feelings helped the situation in any way, they actually made it much worse.

Now, as I mentioned earlier, where people usually get tripped up when they're trying to choose better feeling thoughts, is they try to go from thinking that everything is falling apart to thinking that everything is wonderful. That rarely works because it's too big of a leap. A better strategy is to go from the uncomfortable thought, to the next best thought that you can actually believe right now. So, for example, if you're stressed out and worried about money, it's not realistic to think that you can go from that energetic state, all the way to, "Everything we need will be provided and there's absolutely no problem." It doesn't work. It's too big a leap. You don't actually believe that.

However, you might be able to get yourself - as I did on that bathroom floor - to something like, "Right now, right here in this moment, we have everything we need." Or, "It's entirely possible that we will figure this all out." Experiment with finding just the very next best thought that you can actually believe and, like the first step on a ladder, start deliberating moving your focus and energy up to that slightly better feeling thought and leaving behind the old one. Then, once you can fully believe that one, like the next step on the ladder, look for a slightly better one to move up to and so on.

Gratitude is always an excellent place to go if you're struggling to identify a better feeling thought because gratitude is always a better feeling thought and you can almost always find something to feel grateful for no matter where you are or what you're dealing with. You cannot feel stress and gratitude in the same instant so, start crowding out the stress or anger or fear with more gratitude.

Just remember that you can choose better thoughts. You can choose to be the creator of your thoughts, rather than the victim of them. As with anything, you'll get better at this the more you do it. So, catch yourself as often as you can throughout the day, whenever you're feeling a negative thought and see if you can deliberately and intentionally choose a better thought to energize.

In addition to choosing a thought that feels better, you can also start looking for an activity (other than eating) that will trigger a better feeling.

As we saw earlier, it's important to remember that uncomfortable feelings are actually surprisingly helpful signposts and one of the things they can direct you towards are areas where your body, mind and soul might require a little attention. Sometimes we're feeling exhausted, depleted and overwhelmed, not so much because of what's going around us, but because we're not taking proper care of ourselves. We're not getting enough sleep, not connecting with the people we love and not making time for the activities and rituals that fill our cup.

We'll talk much more about self-care including what it should look like, how often you need it and how to find the time later on when I introduce you to Pillar Five.

Take it minute by minute

Often the feelings we're trying to avoid feel huge and overwhelming which is why we so often end up turning to food to avoid them. Allowing the feeling or the craving without doing anything about it appears like an impossible task. But do you remember that old saying: "How do you eat an entire elephant?" and the answer was, "One bite at a time." It's the same with feeling a big feeling like stress, worry, boredom or a craving for sugar, you allow the feeling one minute at a time or one second at a time if you need to.

When you feel that uncomfortable feeling and your brain is screaming at you to run away towards food to make it better, stop and see if you can feel the stress or the anxiety or even the craving for just a minute without reaching for the food. Then, can you do it for one more minute? Notice your breath and try to relax. See how many seconds or minutes you can string together. Before you know it, the craving may no longer be as white hot as it was at the beginning. The power may be back in your court and you may feel more able to make a healthier choice.

When that happens, notice how it felt to ride that wave and whether that storm. Notice that you felt the feeling and didn't explode. You didn't crumple onto the floor and die. In fact, now that you sat and breathed through the worst of it, it feels much more manageable, and feeling in control like that actually feels pretty fantastic.

Going through this minute by minute exercise not only helps you get through cravings but it actually starts to reprogram that old operating system in your brain that's been driving your unhealthy food habits and patterns. As you do this exercise again and again and sit with the feelings without reaching for the food, you'll start to train your brain to see that it can actually handle the feeling and that, in fact, it feels pretty great to take back control!

Delayed Gratification Exercise

If you're new to this, at the beginning you might want to try combining the NAIL steps with a simple delayed gratification exercise.

For example, say you're desperately craving a brownie, tell yourself you *will* have the brownie but you'll have it in 10 minutes. Set a timer, and while you're waiting, go through the NAIL steps: Name the feeling, allow it to be there with you, investigate the thought behind it and look for a better feeling thought or a healthier activity that will make you feel better.

For those 10 minutes, feel the feelings, knowing that in a few minutes you can make them go away with the brownie. Eventually of course we want to eliminate the brownie altogether, but sometimes you need to start with baby steps. It feels less terrifying for your brain to think that it only has to feel the feelings for 10 minutes rather than telling it that it can't have the treat it's craving at all, but it still allows you to do some important investigative work and start to reprogram some of those old neural pathways in your brain around how you're using food.

But why do we overeat when we're feeling good?

Now, what's interesting is that "feel the feelings" doesn't just apply to uncomfortable, unpleasant feelings. It also applies to the *good* feelings. Tell me if this sounds familiar: you're at a party or on vacation, you're having a good time, you get caught up in all the excitement and energy and, before you know it, you've polished off four margaritas and a huge plate of nachos!

So many people say to me, "Okay, I get why I sabotage myself when I'm feeling miserable, but why do I do it when I'm feeling happy? Why do I do it when I'm out with friends having a great time, or on vacation? I don't want to avoid those feelings – they're awesome!" Well, I would offer that – on some level – you are avoiding those feelings. I know, it sounds counter-intuitive, but hear me out.

First, intense feelings – even good ones – cause a stress response in the body. Our brains don't like change. Change is stressful. So, even happy, exciting events like parties or vacations, feel stressful for your body and your brain and thus, often result in us reaching for food to manage those feelings. Food feels safe and comforting and when we're out of our normal routine, even when it's something fun like a vacation, it makes your brain nervous.

Second, I would argue that, even when the feelings are good ones of connection, love and laughter, you still may not truly be allowing them. You may still not be "feeling the feelings."

Our brains – thanks to dopamine – often have this idea that, if this is good, more would be better. Remember how we learned that dopamine's big message to get you to hunt and gather is: This is going to be great, keep going, you're almost there!" Because of this, we tend to respond to happy events like parties and vacations by wanting *more*. We figure that if we're feeling good now, imagine how much better we'd feel if we also added in our favourite foods?!

But, what if, when the excitement and good energy came at you, you simply sat with it? What if you simply allowed the joy? Allowed the love? Allowed the happiness? Even if it felt unfamiliar or even undeserved? What if you just felt the feelings, acknowledged the discomfort that might accompany them, and made the choice to lean into gratitude instead of nachos? What if you slowed down and allowed yourself to feel satisfied with the good time you were already having instead of letting dopamine send you on a mission for more?

"And I love that!"

There's another little trick that Kyle Cease shares in his New York Times bestselling book, *I Hope I Screw this Up*, that I just love. You can experiment with this when you're trying to break the pattern of using food to avoid uncomfortable feelings.

Start by going through the four NAIL steps and when you figure out the thought that's driving your food craving, say that thought to yourself (or out loud if you're brave), followed immediately by, "And I love that!"

So, for example, "I feel totally overwhelmed at work and I'm afraid that I'm going to drop the ball and my boss will be mad...and I love that!!" Or, "I have no idea how we're going to pay all our bills this month...and I love that!" I know that it sounds crazy and ridiculous but in the weirdest way, it actually often works.

The reason is works is because your brain absolutely loves to be right. So, if you emphatically and loudly declare, "And I love that!!" well, the first thing you brain does is go searching for a reason why that could be right.

Maybe it would feel freeing to have your boss finally blow up at you. Maybe you two could get some stuff out on the table and deal with it. Maybe you could finally tell her or him that there's way too much on your plate. Maybe it would feel really good to have this all be out in the open. Maybe you hate your job and while getting fired would be terrifying, it might also be totally liberating! Who knows what might come up for you, but I'm telling you that it very often works as a way to start reframing some of those negative thought loops that keep us stuck, so it's worth a try!

PILLAR THREE: Feel the Feelings
TRY THIS

Feelings are trying to tell you something - Every feeling has a message for us. If a feeling persists, ask it what it wants to tell you. Sit quietly and allow the answer to appear. Remember that just because you become aware of the message, doesn't mean that you need to "fix" it right now.

Every feeling comes from a thought - If you're feeling something strong (good or bad), it's because of a thought you're having. The situation is never the problem, it's always the thought you're having about it or the meaning that you're giving to it that's creating those feelings. Ask yourself, "What am I making this mean?" or complete the sentence, "The story I'm telling myself here is..."

Feeling the feelings (instead of eating them) – Follow this three-step formula when you feel a craving or catch yourself making a not-so-great choice:

- Take three deep breaths and come into the present moment;

- Do a brain dump if you have the time;

- Use the NAIL steps to help you process the feeling: Name it, Allow it, Investigate it, Look for a better feeling thought and/or activity

Take it one minute at a time - Try not to think of just sitting with the feeling and not eating indefinitely. Just commit to sitting with the feeling without reaching for food for one minute, then try it for one more minute and so on.

Try the delayed gratification exercise – When you're desperately craving a brownie, tell yourself you will have the brownie but you'll have it in 10 minutes. Set a timer, and while you're waiting, go through the NAIL steps. For those 10 minutes, feel the feelings, knowing that in a few minutes you can make them go away with the brownie. Eventually you'll want to do away with the brownie altogether, but this exercise is a great baby step to help you get to where you want to go.

Why do we also overeat when we feel good? - Because we're still not truly feeling the feelings. We're not feeling the joy, happiness, connection and love, rather we're looking for more! Instead, try simply sitting with the happy feelings and leaning into gratitude rather than striving to make them better with food.

"And I love that!"- Once you've identified the thought that's fueling your feeling, try saying it out loud followed by "...and I love that!" This exercise might seem silly, but it's crazy how well

TURNING OFF THE TAP

it works!

Chapter 10

PILLAR FOUR: Disrupt Old Programming

Earlier we talked about how the primary reason that most of us struggle to stay on track with healthy eating actually has nothing to do with a lack of willpower, commitment or quick and healthy recipe ideas. Rather, it's that we're trying to run new behaviors on top of an old, outdated operating system in our brains. It doesn't work because they don't match. And the fact is that we'll never be able to stick with making healthy choices consistently until we first update that old operating system so that it matches the new healthy lifestyle we want to create.

You could discover the absolute perfect diet, eating approach or set of quick and healthy meal ideas, but you will never be able to stick with any of it if you don't first do the work to update that old operating system. It will just keep dragging you back to your old ways again and again because that's what it's currently programmed for.

Each of the first three pillars are absolutely key to updating your old operating system. It's essential that you:

- Get out of auto-pilot (Pillar One)

- Know where you're going (Pillar Two), and

- Feel the feelings (Pillar Three)

However, there are also a few other tools and techniques that you can use specifically to disrupt your brain's old programming. This is how you start to break up those old neural pathways that are no longer serving you and create new ones that will act as a solid

147

foundation for the new, healthier lifestyle you want to create - your new operating system.

Some of these tools are things that you'd do on a daily basis and that create a cumulative effect over time, and some you can use right in the moment when you're wrestling with a big scary craving to help you work with your brain's natural wiring to make a better choice.

Intentional Living

If you take nothing else away from this book, I want you to understand that the real key to breaking old neural pathways and creating new ones is to start living your life with greater *intention*. So much of what we do and think every day is simply an automatic repetition of exactly what we did and thought yesterday and the day before that and the day before that.

If we want to change our lives it's absolutely imperative that we break that spell, take back the reins, climb back into the driver's seat and start living our lives with more purpose and intention. This means waking up, getting clear on the vision you're creating for yourself and more deliberately and consciously choosing the thoughts you're thinking so that you're also choosing the feelings you're feeling and thus the choices you're making.

Seek out opportunities to get out of your regular routine, even if that means just thinking differently. If it's available to you, I highly recommend doing things like going away on a retreat or taking classes or programs (either in person or online). Reading books, listening to podcasts and seeking out local or online communities of like-minded people are also very effective but, in addition to doing as much of that as you can, one of the most accessible and effective tools for ensuring that this work becomes a regular part of your life is to create an intentional morning routine.

Morning Routine

You can't just get out of bed every day and hope for the best. Well, you can, but if you do that you'll probably end up falling back into your old, familiar patterns and feeling disappointed with your results.

Rather, you want to try to start off your day with purpose and intention. Many of the famously successful people that we admire swear by the power of their morning routines. People like Tony Robbins, Oprah Winfrey and Richard Branson have all talked about the key role that morning routines have played in their success.

A morning routine is simply a series of rituals or practices that you do each morning to put yourself firmly in the driver's seat and take back control of your day. Neuroscience shows us that how you start the day, very often determines how the entire day will go. If you start the day by feeling grumpy, overwhelmed and assuming the worst, guess how things are going to play out for you? And then guess what you're going to be eating later on to manage all that chaos?

Instead, I want you to take back the reins as soon as you wake up and begin to *create* a day that will leave you feeling calm, grounded and successful. This is going to help keep you aligned with your vision, on track towards your goals, and make the healthier choices feel a lot easier and more natural.

How to Create Your Morning Routine

You want to create a morning routine that feels good for you and allows you to start your day feeling grounded, focused and in control. This doesn't need to take a lot of time. Think about giving yourself just 10-45 minutes for this every morning. Yes, it might mean that you have to get up a little bit earlier, but I promise that the positive impact you feel throughout your day, and the better choices you make as a result will be well worth it!

The following are just some of the elements you might want to pick and choose from when building your own morning routine. Take what resonates with you, leave the rest and add in anything else that feels good to you. You're looking for elements that will help get you out of auto-pilot, remind you of the you that you see in your vision and help you feel grounded, focused and in control of your day.

Alter

Don't be intimidated by the term, "alter." All I'm talking about here is a little spot somewhere in your home, maybe a corner of your bedroom or office, maybe a small portion of your desk, where you can create a special space where you can come each day to do your morning routine.

You can decorate this space with things that are meaningful for you, bring you joy and remind you of the vision you have for the person you are stepping into and the life you're creating for yourself. This little alter could include pictures, keep-sakes, crystals, flowers, candles or anything else that reminds you of the person you want to be and the things that are the most meaningful for you.

It's hard to just plop yourself down in your messy bedroom or living room, surrounded by clutter and laundry and then proceed to try to feel focused, peaceful and intentional. Instead, create some kind of area that is special. Make your morning routine a sacred time that deserves its own sacred space.

By creating a spot like this where you come every day to do your morning routine, you begin to train your brain to view coming to this spot as the trigger that it's time to shift into your morning routine.

Meditation

Meditation is such a powerful practice that it's the one element that I would highly encourage you to include in your morning routine - even if you don't include any other elements.

Meditation is a great way to begin your morning routine because it will shift you into a more mindful state where you can be more present, aware and conscious to what's going on around you and within you and you'll then be able to carry this state with you throughout your day and into whatever life throws at you.

You can use a guided meditation or just sit in silence and focus on your breath.

Gratitude

I love to include gratitude in my morning routine because often we've fallen into a habit of starting the morning with worries and stress about the day ahead. By getting into the habit of thinking of or writing down a few things that you're grateful for that day instead, it immediately shifts you out of that energy of fear and scarcity and moves you to an energy of joy, love and appreciation - a much more empowering place.

This is the perfect example of being deliberate and intentional with your thoughts. Those stressful, worrying thoughts might still pop into your head when you wake up, but when you make the choice to replace those disempowering, negative thoughts with positive and energizing thoughts of gratitude, you are taking back control and choosing the kind of thoughts that you're going to let play around up there in your brain.

Set an intention

As I mentioned above, when you wake up each day and simply hope that the day will go well you are stepping out of the driver's seat and giving away your power. Instead, be more intentional about how you're steering your day by setting an intention for where you want to go, how you want to show up and who you want to be today.

For example, if you have a huge To Do list and you're already feeling anxious, maybe your intention is to remember that there is the perfect amount of time do everything. Set that as your intention for the day and every time you find yourself feeling overwhelmed and fantasizing about how nicely a donut would help take the edge off, bring yourself back to that intention you set for yourself that morning. Use it as an anchor to keep you connected to your bigger vision for yourself and keep you on the path that you know will take you there.

Sometimes an intention can simply be a word. Think of a word that encapsulates the way that you want to feel that day. Pick whatever word feels fabulous in your body when you say it to yourself. Think of words like: calm, light, strong, grounded, clear, soft, supported, bold, or true. Set that word as your intention for the day and repeat it in you head as often as you can throughout the day to remind yourself of that intention. You can use the same word day after day, or pick a new word every morning depending on what you feel you need most at that time.

Visualization

We talked a lot about the power of creating a vision and having a daily visualization practice in Pillar Three. Your morning routine is a great place to include that daily visualization.

Close your eyes, call up that incredible vision you created of the future you that you want to step into, and imagine yourself already being her. Spend a few minutes imagining yourself walking around in her body, her clothes, her home, making food and eating the way she would, interacting with your family the way she would, feeling the way she would. You'll find that after just a few minutes, you'll start to feel like you're *actually* her. It should feel wonderful.

Alternatively, you can think about a potentially challenging situation you have ahead of you that day and visualize that higher version of yourself navigating that situation in a way that would feel really great and that you would feel incredibly proud of. What would she do? What would she say? What would she think? How would she feel? How would she react?

Affirmations

I think that affirmations get a bad rap. They've been connected to the self-help world in such an unfortunate way and now people often think of affirmations as empty statements uttered by self-indulgent and whiny narcissists wearing rose-coloured glasses. But before you go rolling your eyes and dismissing them, I encourage you to give affirmations a chance. You may have heard the saying, "Thoughts become things" and personally, I have seen the truth of this in my own life over and over again.

Like attracts like. This is why, when you're feeling miserable and frustrated, you tend to easily find more reasons to feel that way – a bad day typically gets worse before it gets better. It's also why, when you're on vacation and loving life, you feel like you're overflowing with happiness and gratitude! Everything is beautiful! Where your attention goes, your energy flows and this is why positive affirmations can be such powerful tools for change.

Affirmations are like little course correctors that can start moving you from a negative space, to a positive one. They can help shift you from, "I'll never lose the weight," "I can't do this," or "this is too hard," to…

"I am worth the better choice," "the small step I take today will be the beginning of a massive shift," or "today I choose to eat with love."

Feels a whole lot better, right? And the happier you feel, the more happy thoughts and feelings you attract. It's like a snowball rolling downhill. I've seen first-hand how effective these little affirmations can be in improving the food choices we make day-to-day.

There are just two things to consider when you go about creating an affirmation for yourself. First, it must be something you can *believe*. Very often people find that affirmations feel hollow and even silly and that's because they are thinking of affirmations that they don't currently believe.

For example, if you fear that you're never going to be able to lose the weight and keep it off, then an affirmation like, "I will lose the weight effortlessly and never gain it back," doesn't work for you because you don't currently believe that. It's too big of a jump. The secret to finding a powerful affirmation is to create one that moves you to a better feeling thought but is still something you can believe. So, you might consider something like the wonderful quote from Glennon Doyle, "I can do hard things." Or Marie Forleo's, "Everything is figure-out-able." Perhaps that's something that simultaneously makes you feel good and is also something that (hopefully) you can believe.

Second, it must be something that feels really good. Don't create an affirmation that you think you *should* believe. You must create an affirmation that makes you feel wonderful when you think it to yourself or say it out loud. You might need to play around with a few different versions and different words to get it just right, but just keep trying until you get closer and closer and eventually you'll know it in your body when you've hit on a good one.

Journaling

Journaling as part of your morning routine can be a great way to calm your thoughts and get some clarity around your intention for the day ahead.

Don't overthink this. Simply crack open your journal and start writing whatever's in your head. Whatever you're thinking about or whatever's worrying you. Write about a dream you had. Write about some of the bigger life questions you might have been mulling over lately. Write about how you're feeling right now and why you're feeling that way. Write about what you're afraid of and what you're excited about.

This isn't about writing anything specific or meaningful, it's simply the act of writing down anything that's going on in your head. Whatever you write is right. No one but you is ever going to read this. This is simply about getting the chatter in your head to quiet down by getting it out of you and onto the paper. The act of writing things down in this way can very often help you start the day from a place of greater calm, peace and strength. If you're still struggling with "writer's block," try this simple "3-2-1" exercise that many of my students love.

Open your journal and write down:

3 things you're grateful for. These can be big (family, home, health, etc.) or small (warm bed, sunny day, favourite TV show on tonight).

2 commitments for the day around your health. These are two things that you're going to focus on doing today to improve your health. Pick things that are very small and very specific here (e.g., only one cup of coffee, walking for 30 minutes, vegetables with lunch and dinner, meditating for 15 minutes, etc.).

1 intention or affirmation you want to carry with you. Choose one word or thought that you want to guide you today. Try to write this in the present tense. Here are a few examples: I am enough; my body deserves only the best food; peace flows through my body, mind and soul; I care for my body with respect, love and compassion; I am a powerful creator of my own experience.

Reading

Now, when I say reading, I don't mean the latest Stephen King novel, save that for later when you're curled up with a cup of tea in your PJs. What I mean when I suggest reading as part of your morning routine is just a page or two from a book that inspires you and reminds you of your bigger vision and the person you want to become. I suggest either non-fiction or poetry. Self-development books or memoirs can be inspiring and help you think about things in your own life differently. And poetry can speak to your soul in a way that almost nothing else can.

Those are some of my favourite morning routine elements that you can pick and choose from. There are many others that might also feel good for you including: pulling an oracle card; using essential oils; prayer; movement such as running, stretching, yoga or dance; or a warm cup of herbal or green tea.

Think of how much time you can devote to a morning routine for yourself and then pick and choose the elements that you want to include in yours. For example, maybe you have 30 minutes that you're willing to give to yourself every morning. You could meditate for ten minutes, followed by three minutes of visualization, two minutes of affirmations and then 15 minutes of journaling during which you also decide on an intention you want to set for your day. Done!

Or maybe you do 15 minutes of meditation followed by five minutes of writing down a list of things you're grateful for, then 10 minutes of reading that inspires you and end by picking an oracle card to set your intention for the day. Voila!

Create a morning routine that feels great for *you*. This isn't something you're doing for me or for anyone else. This is a gift that you're giving to yourself. What would feel wonderful to you? Try different things. Your morning routine can change every day if you want it to. All that matters is that you give yourself that time consistently every day to deliberately and intentionally set the trajectory for your day ahead. No more waking up, letting life happen and hoping for the best!

Regardless of what yours ends up looking like, a morning routine will help you - on a daily basis - start to disrupt the old wiring of auto-pilot and those old patterns of self-sabotage. Over time you'll start to notice yourself being more aware, more deliberate and more intentional in your thoughts, your reactions and your choices.

In addition, I also want to share with you a few other tools and techniques that you can start using to begin to disrupt that old programming that's been keeping you stuck:

Out of sight, out of mind

Our brains prefer immediate gratification. This phenomenon is also known as "delay discounting" and it means that **the further away a reward appears, either in space or time, the less appealing it is to you.**

This is, in part, because your brain's reward system did not evolve to respond to future rewards. Remember that this part of your brain is still working in much the same way it did back in caveman days when survival was the key driver of daily life. In that context, a reward that was far off – whether 10 miles or 10 days – was pretty much useless.

As soon as you create any distance between yourself and the temptation, you immediately take power away from the brain's reward centre (limbic brain) and give it back to your brain's self-control system (pre-frontal cortex). This can even be done when the temptation is staring you right in the face like with food at a party, or the all-you-can-eat buffet on vacation.

In the now famous Stanford Marshmallow Experiment done in the late 1960s and early 1970s, children were given a single marshmallow and told that, if they could resist it for 10 min while the researchers left the room, they'd be rewarded with two marshmallows! Most of the kids caved and ate the first marshmallow, but the kids who didn't used very interesting techniques to boost their willpower for those 10 important minutes – techniques that we can learn from.

One child described how he imagined a frame around the marshmallow and used that as a way to think of it as a picture, rather than something real. This is a great example of using delay discounting to help yourself make better choices. By imagining that the marshmallow was just a picture, it made the reward less present and thus, less tempting.

Other children physically turned away from the marshmallow so they couldn't see it while they waited. Another great example of delay discounting because by removing the temptation from your field of vision, you automatically reduce the perceived proximity of the reward.

You can implement this technique yourself by telling yourself that you'll have the food that you're craving, but you'll have it in 10 minutes and putting it out of sight while you wait. Neuroscientists have discovered that just a 10 minute delay in eating something makes a huge difference in how your brain values that reward because it turns immediate gratification into a future reward (something your brain values far less).

The next time you feel tempted, try this delayed gratification exercise. Tell yourself that you will have the treat, but you'll have it 10 minutes from now. Set the alarm on your phone or watch, put the food out of sight, or remove yourself from the vicinity of the food, and do something else. You can distract yourself with something enjoyable or, as we discussed in the last chapter, use the time to get curious about what you're feeling and thinking right now that is making the food so tempting.

Once the 10 minutes are over, tune in and determine whether or not you still want the food. If you do, that's fine, you still did some good work in disrupting those old neural pathways, and if you don't – yay you!!

Keep an Evidence Journal

Updating your old operating system is about getting out of your old patterns and ruts, not just in terms of your behaviors, but perhaps even more importantly in terms of how you think.

In Dr. Michael Shermer's book *The Believing Brain* he explains: "We form our beliefs for a variety of subjective, personal, emotional, and psychological reasons in the context of environments created by family, friends, colleagues, culture, and society at large; after forming our beliefs we then defend, justify, and rationalize them with a host of intellectual reasons, cogent arguments, and rational explanations. Beliefs come first, explanations for beliefs follow.

We can't help believing. Our brains evolved to connect the dots of our world into meaningful patterns that explain why things happen. These meaningful patterns become beliefs. Once beliefs are formed the brain begins to look for and find confirmatory evidence in support of those beliefs, which adds an emotional boost of further confidence in the beliefs and thereby accelerates the process of reinforcing them, and round and round the process goes in a positive feedback loop of belief confirmation, ensuring that we are always right."

In simpler terms, what Dr. Shermer is saying is that we form a belief such as, "I'm addicted to sugar" for a variety of social and emotional reasons and we then subconsciously seek out evidence that supports that belief and become blind to any evidence that would contradict it. By doing this we create a perceived experience that we are always right.

Remember how we talked about how dopamine works in your brain? And remember how we saw that sugar, fat, pinging slot machines, shopping and social media give your brain a nice dopamine hit? Well, guess that else give you brain a hit of dopamine? Yup, being right. And this is because being right means safety and predictability and (as we know) those are your brain's favourite things.

But, when your brain starts to defend your old limiting beliefs you're in dangerous territory because your life is now limited to the box inside your story. You will only see things that support the belief, and you will miss things that differ from the belief. And now, your limiting beliefs are running your life.

For example, if we would like to lose weight but we haven't been able to so far, we create a belief around that such as "I have no willpower," or "I'm weak," or "I'll never lose the weight." We ascribe that meaning and create that belief and then our brain immediately starts looking for evidence to support it (and starts ignoring or disregarding evidence that challenges it). For example, "See! I ate that cupcake, I knew I had no willpower!"

This is why I ask clients to keep an Evidence Journal. This is a little notebook they carry with them or a digital note in their phone in which they track every single healthy choice they make each day. When they want a third cup of coffee but don't get it, they write it down. When they choose the vinaigrette dressing instead of the ranch, they write it down. When someone brings donuts into the office and they avoid the break room so they don't have any, they write it down.

After a week of doing this every day I have them sit down on the weekend, go back and read over all the healthy choices they made. Sometimes there are pages and pages to go through. When it's all down on paper in front of them, they begin to see that they actually *do* have willpower, they actually make *lots* of healthy choices every day and they actually *have* avoided sugar many times throughout the week.

This is often shocking for people and is the only way they can force their brain to see that the belief they have that they've been basing their identity on (I'm someone who is addicted to sugar), is actually false. This is another way that old wiring gets broken down and new wiring gets formed.

Marinate in Your Wins

What many of us tend to do is spend a whole lot of time thinking about our not-so-great choices, and very little time thinking about our excellent choices. When we eat the leftover birthday cake for breakfast we beat ourselves up about it for the rest of the day, but when we get a workout in before dinner we barely acknowledge it except perhaps to berate ourselves for not working out harder or longer. This is a problem for two reasons and they both have to do with the fact that your brain is wired to avoid pain and seek pleasure. In other words, your brain is always looking for a reward.

First, beating yourself up feels awful and, as a result, tends to steer your brain towards reward-seeking behavior (a.k.a. eating junk food), which means that the more we beat ourselves up and judge ourselves, the more we want to eat.

Second, when making the healthy choices always feels like deprivation and pain and never feels like a reward, our brains never want to do it. It's as simple as that.

The solution? Find and focus on the reward within the healthy behavior. So, when you get that workout in (no matter how it went), take a few minutes in your car or at home later to feel proud of yourself. Acknowledge the fact that you made a choice to take care of yourself, to put yourself first, to love and honour your mind, body and soul. Let those good feelings well up inside of you and then "marinate" in them for a few minutes. Let them wash over you and seep into your cells until you feel absolutely on top of the world. This is how you start to reprogram that part of your old operating system that tells you that making the healthy choices is hard and no fun. This is how you train your brain to start viewing the healthy choices as the reward its looking for.

161

So, the next time you get that workout in, or make the better choice at the restaurant, or eat just half the cookie, don't just gloss over it. Take some time to tap into how proud of yourself you are and how good that feels and sit in that feeling until you absorb it into every cell in your body.

Reframe your idea of a "treat"

"You deserve it," the little voice in your head whispers. "You're tired, you've had such a busy week, you've got an even busier day ahead, you've eaten so well all week – you deserve this treat. Go for it!"

I know I'm not alone in this. I know this little voice is in your head too. So, what should you do when it starts whispering in your ear? How can you resist? Try reframing what a "treat" means for you. Stop and ask yourself, "what do I really deserve?"

Because here's the thing, "You deserve this" presupposes that "this" (the croissant, or the donut, or the fries with gravy, or the bowl of ice cream) is a real treat, something really wonderful and a lovely gift to give yourself. And that's the lie.

Because here's just a small snapshot of what foods like these do once inside your body:

- Spike your blood sugar, forcing your pancreas to quickly pump out buckets of insulin in a desperate attempt to stabilize those blood sugar levels before you fall into a coma;
- Beat up your adrenal glands (which are likely already exhausted from stress and poor sleep) by forcing them to kick in and work to balance the influx of sugar;
- Set off a massive inflammatory response from your immune system that spreads throughout your tissue and joints;

162

- Exhaust your liver by forcing it to break down huge amounts of fructose;
- Spike your stress hormones and cause a massive stress response through your brain and entire body.

It's actually a pretty brutal and relentless attack. Eating these things is much more an act of abuse than love. So, the next time that little voice starts whispering in your ear, "You deserve it," stop and ask yourself what you *really* deserve? Do you deserve to be brutalized, beaten and wounded from the inside?

Maybe what you actually deserve is a nap. Or a gorgeous, sweet fruit salad. Or a short session of juicy yoga stretches and restorative poses. Or a good laugh over the phone with your best friend. Or a cuddling session with your kids, partner or pet. Or a walk all by yourself.

Reframe what it means to give yourself a "treat" and ask yourself what you really deserve. Instead of "I can't have that," think, "I don't want that."

Focus on just the first step

Often we see changing an old habit as an enormous mountain to climb and the sheer size of the task feels so overwhelming that our brain, which is wired to avoid pain, tells us it's way too hard to even try. This is another sneaky tactic that Resistance uses to keep us in our comfort zone.

To change this old programming, try identifying just the very first step that would need to happen in order for a particular pattern or habit to change and commit to just doing that.

For example, as most writers do, I experienced enormous resistance while writing this book. The project felt overwhelming and too big for me to wrap my brain around. The enormity of it paralyzed me and I would put off writing and procrastinate for ages. As I investigated this feeling further, I came to realize that the very hardest part was simply turning on my laptop and opening the file titled "The Book." That first step felt impossible because it seemed like the beginning of an enormous and complicated journey and I immediately became overwhelmed by everything I would have to do to complete it. But what I found was that if I could limit my focus to conquering only that first step of turning my computer on and opening that file, everything after it felt much easier.

This also often works in a situation like being out at a restaurant with friends. You're staring at the menu and you want to make a healthy choice, but the nachos or fettuccine carbonara would be so good! The idea of depriving yourself of those foods and the fear that your whole evening will be less fun as a result feels like too much to handle so you end up panicking and ordering the junk. But, if you put everything else out of your mind and simply commit to doing nothing more than saying the words, "I'll have the spinach salad with salmon," when the waiter comes to take your order, then the rest is easy. And what you'll find is that the food comes and it's actually really tasty and it's easy to eat it and you feel pretty amazing for having made a choice that aligns with your bigger goals. It's just that first tiny step that's the hardest, so focus only on doing that and leave the rest to sort itself out.

What is the very first tiny step in one of the habits that you want to break or create? If you want to go out for a run every morning, maybe it's simply changing into your running clothes. Commit to just doing that and don't think about what would come after. What you'll find is that, once you have those running clothes on, going for a run doesn't feel like quite such an insurmountable task.

If you want to be more consistent with meal planning, focus on simply pulling out a piece of paper, finding a pen and writing down the days of the week. Commit to just doing that and then see how much easier it feels to keep going.

Can you do it anyway?

I hear a lot of excuses. And I say that with absolutely no judgement. We all do this. Excuses are the tools our brains use to keep us from changing, growing and moving outside of our comfort zones.

Your brain is crafty. It's not going to say to you, "don't go to the gym today because it will be uncomfortable." No, you'd see right through that. Instead, it uses far more rational-sounding excuses like, "I think I might be coming down with a cold so I should probably skip the gym," or "I might as well have that bacon and egg McMuffin this morning because we have that birthday party tonight and I know I'm going to over-eat. I'll start eating healthier tomorrow," or "I don't have time to meditate every day right now. Things will quiet down next month so I'll start then."

For a long time, I approached the excuses that my clients offered in a way that was incredibly ineffective - I tried to reason with them. Have you tried this? It looks like this:

You don't have enough time? Let's look at your calendar and see where we might find some extra time.

Think that cooking healthy food is hard and complicated? Let's pick just one or two new recipes each week for you to try.

It feels overwhelming? Let's try and simplify the steps for you.

What I've since come to realize is that there's no point in trying to argue with excuses. There's no point in trying to come up with viable solutions for them. Excuses are not interested in solutions and they're always going to be more conniving than you and hit right back with another variation. You found some extra time for meal prep? Okay, but you probably don't have the right ingredients in the house so maybe not this week. Sound familiar? It's a game you're never going to win.

So, instead, I've started using a new approach. No matter what the excuse, I simply ask: Can you do it anyway?

When your body tells you it's too hard, too uncomfortable and you've had enough? Okay, can you do it anyway?

When your mind tells you you're not doing it right and you don't have the time or the right tools or the natural ability? Okay, can you do it anyway?

When the mean voice inside your head says you'll almost certainly fail at this and make a fool of yourself? Okay, can you do it anyway?

I understand that you think you're too busy. I know that you think you don't have time or don't know how or it's too hard. I get that you're afraid that you're not doing it right or that you'll fail if you try. I understand it all. But my question for you is, can you do it anyway? Because it's really the only question that matters.

PILLAR FOUR: Disrupt Old Wiring
TRY THIS

Live your life with intention - If we want to change our lives it's absolutely imperative that we snap ourselves out of auto-pilot, take back the reins and start living our lives with more purpose and intention. Seek out opportunities to get out of your regular routine and be diligent about trying to notice how and why you're doing the things you're doing and thinking the things you're thinking as often as you can. Not to judge or even change necessarily, but just to get better at being aware and awake.

Create a morning routine – Give yourself 10-45 minutes every morning to become the creator of your day. Pick and choose from some of the elements we covered. Take what resonates with you, leave the rest and add in anything else at all that feels good to you:

- Alter
- Meditation
- Gratitude

- Set an intention
- Visualization
- Affirmations
- Journaling
- Reading

Out of sight, out of mind - The further away a reward appears, either in space or time, the less appealing it is to you. Use this to your advantage when you're in the middle of a craving and seek to reduce the food's appeal by putting it out of sight and setting a timer for 10 minutes before eating it. After doing that, see if your craving feels less intense and more manageable.

Keep an Evidence Journal - Our brains naturally focus on the negative. As a result we start to create deeply held limiting beliefs about ourselves that we believe we have lots of evidence to support. To rewire this, start writing down every single healthy choice you make every day and sit down and review the list once a week. You'll see how many more healthy choices you actually make. This helps your brain create new empowering beliefs about yourself, who you are and what you're capable of.

Marinate in your wins - Your brain is always seeking reward. Train your brain to register making healthy choices as a reward by pausing and absorbing how fantastic it feels when you're in control and making the healthy choice. Take the time after you make a good choice to let the great feelings seep into your cells.

Reframe your idea of a "treat" - When you hear yourself saying, "I deserve this treat," think about what that food is actually doing to your beautiful body and ask yourself what you truly deserve.

Focus on just the first step - Looking at the entire task or action can appear overwhelming and end up paralyzing us. Instead, pick a habit you'd like to change and focus only on the smallest first step that needs to happen and just do that.

Can you do it anyway? - Allow all the excuses to speak their mind but then ask, "Can I do it anyway?"

Chapter 11

PILLAR FIVE: Fill Your Cup

Too often we're trying to do this healthy living thing backwards. We hit the couch at the end of a long, stressful day and in that moment of exhaustion and utter depletion we make a feeble attempt to resist the junk food, and nine times out of ten we fail miserably. Our response to that is to beat ourselves up ("why can't I have more willpower?") and vow to be better tomorrow. But tomorrow night ends up being exactly the same story and so on and so on.

How do we break this vicious cycle? They key here is to flip things around and instead of trying to make healthy choices in our weakest moment, we need to get ahead of it. We need to reverse engineer our success by anticipating the challenges we'll face later and taking specific actions ahead of time to ensure that we don't fall into those old traps.

Have a Plan

Here's what normally happens, we decide that we're going to eat better, move more and make time for self-care. We tell ourselves that we'll meal plan and prep ahead of time; cook healthy, balanced meals every day; go to the gym or that spin class; and set aside some "me" time. We know how important all of this is. We're tired of feeling like crap and we decide that we're one hundred percent committed to making a full lifestyle change. Let's do this!

Then, a day or a few days or a week goes by and life gets in the way. Work gets busy, we start wondering if we're coming down with a cold, the kids need to be driven to soccer practice or the mall. We miss our window for meal planning and prep. Too many days away from the gym start to stack up, and suddenly we're right back where we started, eating the same old way we always have, sitting on the couch instead of moving our bodies and putting everyone else's needs ahead of our own until we're too exhausted to move.

What happened? Of course we immediately assume that it's because we're not organized enough, too lazy and it's all too hard (how the heck does anyone do all this anyway?).

But what really happened was that we missed a key piece of the puzzle in the middle, right there in between being so excited for our shiny, healthy new life and watching it all fall apart around us, and that piece was a **plan**. We neglected to make a specific and detailed plan for exactly what we were going to do when life came calling and Resistance tried to pull us off course.

We relied simply on willpower to try to make the better choice, but since we were already exhausted our willpower bank account was empty and we were defenceless. We had no other tools on hand to help us stay the course so we fell off track. Instead of setting ourselves up for failure again and again like this, we need to start coming at this a little differently. We tend to act like the fact that we felt tempted to make a not-so-great food choice or lay on the couch is a failure. It's not. That temptation is always going to be there. Remember that our brains are naturally wired to seek out reward.

Instead, we need to recognize that this is *always* going to happen, stop believing that our desire for cookies at night or our preference for the couch over the treadmill indicates some kind of weakness or deficiency on our part, and simply sit down and formulate a plan for exactly what we will do and what tools we will use when we're faced with those choices in the future.

The way you succeed isn't by never again feeling tempted to eat junk food or skip the gym, the way you succeed is by having and executing a specific and detailed plan for what you'll do when you feel that way.

When we try to make a healthy choice in the moment, whether it's saying no to the nachos at the restaurant, or saying yes to the gym when the couch is so darn comfy, we rarely make a good one. There's a number of reasons for this, many of which we've already touched on, but one of them is simply that these days we're almost always trying to make those decisions while in a state of decision fatigue.

Our brains have a finite amount of decision-making power (a.k.a. willpower) each day. Think of it like a bank account that you're making a withdrawal from every time you have to make a decision. In our busy, chaotic modern world we're bombarded by decisions in every moment from every angle. Our limited decision-making power gets used up quickly making it very difficult for us to resist temptation as the day goes on.

The best way to combat this is to take some time when your decision-making power is strong, engage your rational prefrontal cortex and create a specific and detailed plan for exactly what you'll do when you encounter a cue or trigger. This way, when you have to make a choice about what to eat or whether to work out, you don't require nearly as much willpower; you can simply implement the plan.

As you make your plan, keep in mind what we learned earlier about the structure of habit loops. The purpose of your plan is to override an old habit loop so you'll need to keep in mind the *trigger*, decide on a new *behavior* and ensure that there is still some element of *reward*.

For example, say you desperately want to get to the gym three nights a week but have a habit of crashing on the couch with a bowl of sugary or salty snacks once the rest of your family is in bed. Don't wait until you're on the couch to decide what you'll do, instead, examine your cue, routine and reward for this particular habit and make a plan ahead of time for exactly how you'll change it.

So, your cue or trigger for this habit is a combination of a certain time of day (say 10:00pm), a certain dynamic in your home (you're alone and everyone else is in bed), and a certain feeling (exhausted, stressed, depleted, unappreciated). The current behavior is lying on the couch with a bowl of junk food and the reward your brain is looking for is to feel calm and like you're taking care of yourself and getting a treat.

Given all of that information, your plan could be as follows: instead of waiting until 10:00pm rolls around, maybe at 8:00pm you make your way to the gym where you do a 45 min workout followed by 30 minutes of gentle stretching and some time in the hot tub and/or sauna or steam room. Invest in some beautiful organic body lotion or scrub that smells divine and make part of your gym time all about pampering yourself. Then you get home by 10:00pm you can still be on the couch in your cozy PJs watching your favourite show with a warm cup of herbal tea. The couch will feel great and well-deserved and the junky snacks won't have such a pull on you because you already will have given your brain the reward that it used to look to those snacks to provide.

In this way, you create a specific and detailed plan for *exactly* what you'll do when you encounter your cues or triggers in order to get the same, or a similar, payoff. Don't wait until you're in the middle of a trigger to try to decide what to do. You won't make a decision that you'll be happy with later.

When you're making your plan, think about all of the tools you've learned thus far throughout the book. Note which ones feel like they resonate with you and could be a useful part of your plan.

Self-Care

Another way that we can get ahead of it is to stop ending every day utterly exhausted and depleted. We talked earlier about how, almost always, we're using food to avoid uncomfortable feelings and what I've noticed is that the most common uncomfortable feelings we're looking to avoid are stress, overwhelm and exhaustion.

Do you "reward" yourself with junk food at the end of a long, stressful day?

Does the weekend become one long binge-fest justified by the fact that you made it through another crazy week and have another one looming ahead?

Do you ever find yourself knowingly making an unhealthy choice and saying, "I deserve it!" as an excuse?

The truth is – and I'm afraid there's no way of getting around this – if you're using junk food as a way to nurture, soothe and comfort yourself it means that you're not making self-care a big enough priority in your life. I'm sorry, but it's true. And the fact that you say you don't have time for self-care won't make it any less true.

I hear different versions of the same story from so many of my clients. Days spent shuttling kids around, meeting deadlines at work, trying to cram in workouts, declutter the house and stressing the whole time about all the other items on the To Do list that aren't getting done.

"Once I get the kids in bed and the kitchen tidied up and my work finished, it's *my* time," they say. "Time to settle into the couch, flip on my favourite TV show and break out the [insert favourite snack here]."

Do you see what's happening here? Do you see the connection? Your energy and motivation are finite resources and every day you are utterly depleting your cup, squeezing out every last drop and leaving nothing in the tank.

As we know now, when your brain feels depleted (pain) it automatically thinks of the thing that it knows is going to most quickly and easily deliver some relief from that uncomfortable feeling and replace it with a far nicer feeling – food! So you eat. And eat. And eat. And you don't eat broccoli. You eat the sugar and fat that your brain craves for the instant gratification it's looking for.

It's important to implement the first four pillars: get out of auto-pilot, know where you're going, start feeling the feelings instead of avoiding them and disrupt the old wiring in your operating system, but none of those things are going to help you make better choices long-term if you continue to end every day with an empty cup.

"But I'm already too busy!" I hear you say. "I can barely keep up with everything I already have going on, there is simply no space for 'me time.' It sounds great, but it's just never going to happen."

173

Well, then, this pattern you've created with food is never going to change. I'm sorry if that sounds harsh but I say it from a place of deep love and wanting better for you.

It's not a matter of time, it's a matter of *priorities*. Right now you do not make yourself a priority. You make showering a priority. You make laundry a priority. Those things are non-negotiable in your life, right? For example, you would never say, "I love the idea of showering. I can totally see the benefits and I admire other people who shower regularly and are able to balance it with everything else, I personally just don't have time for it."

It's laughable because we would never do that. You make time to shower. Even if it means telling people that you'll be a little late or telling your kids that they need to watch TV while mom has a quick shower. Self-care needs to be on the same level. It's no less important.

So, let's talk about what we actually mean when we talk about "self-care." When I talk about self-care, I'm not necessarily talking about bubble baths and spa days. Those are lovely but I consider those pampering rather than self-care. When I talk about self-care, I'm talking about something deeper. I'm talking about consciously making time for activities, practices and rituals that foster a sense of connection.

"Connection with what?" you might ask. Connection on three different levels:

- Connection with the deepest, truest version of yourself;

- Connection with the people you love and who know and love you the most; and

- Connection with something greater than yourself (whatever you like to call that: Mother Nature, the universe, God, Shakti, etc.).

Why are these three areas of connection so important? Well, imagine a tree; a tree with thin, shallow roots is quickly washed away in a storm. But a tree with deep, strong roots grounding it into the earth is almost impossible to push over no matter what gets thrown at it.

When we're making self-care a priority, we're spending time practicing and strengthening that deep sense of connection on a daily basis and that becomes our deep root system so that, when external factors bombard us (as they will), we're ready and we can stand in that place of strength and power and weather the storm without being pushed over.

Think of self-care as they way you grow that deep and complex root system for yourself. You do that work every day to grow and spread those strong roots and then when you're pushed, you're not easy to budge.

Moreover, as human beings, we're simply wired for connection. We're social animals and we're also highly self-aware animals. Because of this, I believe that when we feel disconnected from our true selves, from the people we love and from our place in the universe, we suffer. Thus, when we start to feel the lack of any of these three areas of connection, we start to mistakenly seek them out in things like shopping, social media, celebrity gossip and food. These things are low hanging fruit. They're quick, easily accessible and artificially mimic true connection. They also give our brains an instant hit of dopamine which gives us a little "high" and temporarily numbs the ache of the disconnection we feel. But it's not an effective long-term solution because it's not addressing the real need. So, as much as we might enjoy a massage or a spa day, they likely won't do the trick to provide that feeling of connection that we require. You don't need to cancel your massage appointment but think of that as more like pampering or general physical health care rather than true self-care.

For true, deep self-care, we must seek out those activities and experiences that make us feel most connected to ourselves, to the people we love and who love us back, and to an energy greater than ourselves. And these things are going to be different for everyone. What makes me feel connected to myself and to the universe, might not be what gives you that feeling.

That means that, when choosing self-care practices and rituals, you should always be led only by what lights you up. Don't go to a pilates class every week just because you think you're *supposed* to do pilates as part of self-care. Don't take bubble baths if you hate sitting in a tub of soapy water.

Now, be careful here that you're being led by what feels good to your *heart* and not what feels good to your *brain*. Your brain may tell you that lying on the couch and eating potato chips would feel really good, but I promise you that if you really tune inward and listen, that's not what your heart is saying.

I'm going to share with you 12 different self-care practices and rituals that you can pick and choose from. The first nine are ones that I think you're probably already fairly familiar with. But the last three may be new to you. Notice which ones resonate with you and which do not. Also think about what activities might not be listed here but that you know make you feel that kind of deep connection either with yourself, with others or with something greater that makes you feel like you've come home.

Meditation

We've touched on mediation several times already but I'm going to keep repeating it until it becomes part of your daily life.

Many people feel intimidated by meditation. They say they don't know how to do it or that they simply can't "turn off their brain." But the truth is that everyone can meditate and more and more research is coming out every day about the incredibly powerful rejuvenating effect it has on the brain and body. Even just 10 min a day can offer noticeable benefits. If you want some help getting started and are looking for some guided meditations, check out one of the amazing free apps available for download or search YouTube and see what you find.

Time spent in nature

Getting outside and closer to our natural environment is a great way to de-stress and soothe the central nervous system. Mother Nature's energy is powerful and the more time you spend with her, the more energized you will feel. Seek out forest walks and hikes around your area, do some gardening, plan a day on a beach or just take a picnic to a local park and sit under a tree.

Trees, plants, soil and bodies of water all have high energetic frequencies and the more time we spend around them, near them, touching them, the more our own vibrational frequencies are raised and the more connected we feel to the massive ecosystem that we play an integral part in.

Human connection

Humans are social animals. We're hard-wired to crave connection to one another. Even the most introverted among us can feel the benefit of a good laugh with friends or a loving shoulder to cry on. Try to carve out time in your calendar each week to grab a meal or coffee with friends, take a walk with your partner or call someone you love.

Also, this doesn't need to only be connection with people we know and love. You can experience connection with people in your community by joining a local service organization or community choir. And, volunteering your time to be of service to complete strangers can also be enormously nourishing to the soul.

Time with animals

Animals are deeply intuitive and can sense when your energy is low or when you're feeling down. They offer pure, unconditional love and there's a great deal of research showing that people who have pets live longer, healthier lives. If you're a pet owner, make some time in your day to do nothing but connect with your furry friend. If you don't have a pet in your home, consider volunteering at a local animal shelter or offer to walk your neighbor's dog.

Writing

For many people, writing is extremely therapeutic. With so many thoughts and feelings racing through your head, writing them down can be a great way to make some sense of it all. But you don't have to just write about yourself. Journaling is enjoyable for some, but for others, maybe working on that novel you've been daydreaming about for years or writing poetry feels better. Grab a notepad or open up your laptop, free up your mind and see where the words take you.

Reading

There are few things more lovely than curling up with a good book and being carried away by an enchanting story and compelling characters. If there's nothing good on your nightstand, ask your friends or local librarian for recommendations or check out Amazon or Goodreads to see what others have loved.

I also always encourage people to try reading something new and different – something you wouldn't normally read. Learn something new, open your mind to new ideas and new ways of thinking about the world around you. Joining a local book club can be a great way to find new things to read and also connect with people in your community (two for one!).

Prayer

Prayer is a ritual that is often associated only with organized religions, but I think we can expand that definition. I think that prayer can be whatever feels good in your body. You can pray to someone, you can pray to the universe, you can pray to the sun or moon, you can even pray to yourself.

And praying doesn't need to require detailed knowledge of sacred texts or be complicated. I love writer Anne Lamott's theory that there are really only three prayers: "Help," "Thank you," and "Wow!" What could be simpler?

Yoga

As with meditation, some people are intimidated by yoga and believe they're "not flexible enough" to do it. But, despite the photos you see on Instagram, yoga has nothing to do flexibility and everything to do with working exactly where you are right now. The yoga asanas (or postures) have been handed down over thousands of years and, in addition to being physically strengthening and restorative, they provide a conduit to deep connection with the energy that flows through you and every other living thing in the universe.

If you've never done yoga before, be brave and find a beginner or gentle yoga class near you or check out online offerings from sites like YogaGlo. If you love yoga but haven't been going lately, take out your calendar, look at the local studio's schedule and make a commitment to get to a class this week.

Or, if you feel intimidated by yoga, consider doing something as simple as getting down on the floor and just moving and stretching in whatever way your body wants to move. Put on some music that you love, close the door and just move – no rules.

Tea

Tea ceremonies have long played an important role in the world of Zen Buddhism. The brewing, serving and consumption of tea is considered by Buddhist monks to be the perfect opportunity for cultivating mindfulness and, as a result, has become a sacred part of their path to enlightenment.

These days, herbal teas are one of my favourite ways to treat myself and relax at the end of a long day. Splurge on a beautiful pot and mug to really make a ritual out of the preparation and presentation of the tea. Experiment with different herbs and flowers that are known to have soothing properties such as chamomile, lemon balm, passionflower and valerian.

Make a beautiful cup of tea the way you recharge and treat yourself, rather than a hunk of processed fat and sugar.

Getting Creative

Most of us spend a disproportionate amount of time using our left brain – that's the side that is very analytical and concerned about rules and lists and accomplishing things. Our right brain - the side that colours outside the lines and knows how purple smells does not get the same attention. Spending more time using your right brain can help you feel more balanced, recharged and connected to your truest self. Think about a creative project you enjoy or would like to try (painting, pottery, knitting, playing the piano, etc.) and make time and space for it in your calendar.

Aromatherapy

Our sense of smell is one of the most powerful of our five senses and has a significant effect on our neurochemistry. Engaging this sense as part of your self-care routine can be very effective. If this interests you, try infusing your space with high quality essential oils, burning sage, naturally scented candles or incense. Do your research and find scents that trigger the feelings you're looking for whether that be calm and peaceful or alive and energized.

Okay, so those are the self-care practices and rituals that that may already have thought of. But in this chapter, I want to take you a little deeper and introduce three other areas that might surprise you but that I think are absolutely integral to a discussion of self-care.

Boundaries

I often say that setting boundaries is one of the most powerful acts of self-care. But the truth is that it's also one of the hardest and, as a result, one that we tend to let slide. Generally, we don't like to say "no" to people. If someone asks us to do something, we want to say "yes." We want them to be happy. We want them to like us and think, "What a nice person she is!" We may even really want to do what's being asked of us. But the truth is that our time, energy and focus are finite. And, as I pointed out earlier, if we keep giving them away all day, every day, to everyone else, we end up exhausted, depleted, empty and reaching for food to replenish.

Moreover, if what's being asked of us doesn't align with the greater vision we have for ourselves, we are not serving ourselves or our purpose in the world by saying "yes" simply so that people will like us. I read something the other day that said, "Confidence isn't 'they will like me.' Confidence is 'I'm okay if they don't.'" I think that's really important to remember.

Setting boundaries and saying "no" is something I'm always working on getting better at. It's hard. Recently I said "no" to two people. They did not say, "Good for you for setting boundaries!" They did not congratulate me for my commitment to self-care or tell me that they were proud of me and respected my decision. One seemed a little annoyed and the other was downright disappointed in me. That felt awful and I immediately wondered if I was doing the right thing. I want people to like me too! But it was the right thing for me and that's what I need to be led by. I'm no good to myself or anyone else if I'm allowing other people's needs and priorities to use up my time, energy and focus.

A good tool to use when you're working to establish boundaries is a **decision matrix**. This will help you measure every request you get for some of your time, energy or focus and determine whether to say yes or no. You create a decision matrix by determining what your top three priorities in life are right now. These will likely change significantly over time but decide what they are for you today. To help you out, here is my current list of priorities (in order of importance):

1) Myself

2) My family

3) My clients and the community I serve

If a request or opportunity isn't serving any of those priorities directly, then it's a "no." Even if it's something that sounds cool or fun or interesting. And if people don't like me for that, or think I'm being selfish or inconsiderate or unhelpful – and some of them will - that's okay. Remember that old saying that, "What other people think about your is none of your business."

Think about what your top three priorities are right now. Then, using that as your lens, consider what things you need to say "yes" to more often to support those, and also what things you need to say "no" to more often to protect them.

The Thoughts We Think

Sometimes the only connection we make between our thoughts and our health is around cravings and willpower. "I wish I didn't always want the junk." But I hope you can see, after so many of the things we've covered together so far, that your thoughts actually play and enormous role in your health – physical, mental and spiritual.

Thoughts become things. What you think and believe - these are powerful messages you're sending to yourself and out into the universe. So, when you're constantly thinking that things never work out for you, that "if something can go wrong, it will go wrong," or that you have no willpower, are lazy or that you're "probably never going to lose the weight," that's what you tend to create. This is why it's so important that we're conscious and careful with our thoughts. Because they are powerful forces of creation. The more you think it, the more power you give it.

But the great news is that you get to choose. You get to choose your thoughts. You may not think you do, but you do. Some thoughts we've had so many times over so many years that they have become automatic – a bad habit. But that doesn't mean they still can't be changed. It just means that we need to work a little harder and be a little more diligent about changing them.

Start to notice the negative, unsupportive, unproductive thoughts that loop through your head on auto-pilot. Call out that Mean Voice and its Top 10 Greatest Hits and practice catching yourself in those old habits and *choosing* a different thought.

Integrity

What do we mean when we say that someone has integrity? We

182

mean that they're honest, that they do what they say they're going to do, that we know we can trust them. We know that when we act with integrity, it feels good. And, we've all acted in a way that's out of integrity (be honest) and we know that doesn't feel so good. This is because when we make choices from a place of integrity, we are aligned with a higher vibration within ourselves. It resonates with something greater and it feels...right.

So, what does all this have to do with our relationship with food and with self-care? I believe, a whole lot! Think about how it feels when you interact with another person and they continually act in a way that lacks integrity. Over time they teach you that their actions do not line up with their words. You do not believe that they'll do what they say they're going to do. You begin to lose trust in them and you find yourself disconnecting with them more and more. It doesn't feel good to be with someone who lacks integrity.

So, let's consider this in terms of our relationship with food and self-care. When you tell yourself over and over and over again that you're going to eat better or move more or put a greater emphasis on self-care, and then you choose actions that don't line up with those words, you are acting in a way that lacks integrity.

When your higher self knows that you are endlessly capable and possessing infinite potential and purpose, and then you continually judge yourself, put yourself down and repeat limiting beliefs about yourself, you are *thinking* in a way that lacks integrity.

And all of that takes a toll on your soul. Over time, every time you do those things, it chips away at the trust you have for yourself. You begin to not like yourself so much because it doesn't feel so good to be with yourself when you lack integrity in your actions and your thoughts.

I see this everywhere. People who have spent years struggling with food and their bodies, often carry with them a deep sadness. It's my belief that this lack of integrity within themselves is the root source of that sadness.

Take some time to sit with this notion of integrity. Think about where, when it comes to your health, you are acting with integrity and where you lack integrity. Then, start to take some small steps to move increasingly towards a place of integrity. How do you start living with more integrity in your relationship with yourself? **You make promises to yourself and you keep them.**

It doesn't matter what it is but pick something very small, very doable and very specific that you know you can follow through on. Maybe it's meditating for five minutes on Monday, Wednesday and Friday morning this week. Or, maybe it's starting the day with a glass of lemon water as soon as you wake up every day for the next seven days. Pick something very small and very specific. Make the promise to yourself and keep your promise. And once you've met your goal and kept your promise to yourself, sit with that, acknowledge that you've kept your promise to yourself and acted with enormous integrity and feel how that resonates within you. Feel how good it feels to be able to trust yourself.

Over time, as you collect kept promises, you will slowly begin earn back your own trust. You will be increasingly acting from a place of integrity and you will feel a deep shift inside.

As I said at the beginning of this chapter, if you're using junk food as a way to nurture, soothe and comfort yourself it means that you're not making self-care a big enough priority in your life. Really think about the areas and aspects of self-care that I've introduced you to here, pick a few that resonate with you (remember when choosing self-care practices and rituals to always be led by what lights you up) and make a commitment to make them a non-negotiable part of your every day.

Daily tasks as self-care

We've already talked about the importance of making self-care into a non-negotiable priority like showering or doing laundry, but I also want to offer that self-care need not be only found in activities that we label as "self-care." If we believe that self-care is less about pampering and more about cultivating and practicing connection, then you can make almost any activity - including many daily chores or tasks such as washing the dishes, cleaning the cat litter box, folding laundry, or meal prep into an exercise in self-care.

When you do these activities in a present and mindful way, being slow and deliberate and changing your perception of them from being *chores* to being an expression your "dharma" (your purpose) then you are cultivating connection to your truest self, and – ta da - this previously frustrating and boring activity has just become a form of self-care simply by you changing your perception of it.

"I wash the dishes, not because I *have* to, or because everyone else left them for me to do because they don't appreciate how hard I work, etc." But rather, "I wash the dishes because washing the dishes is a practice that aligns with my purpose (i.e., creating a clean, healthy home; caring for my family, etc.)." In this way, washing the dishes becomes spiritual work.

Self-Love

Now, I know that this isn't the first time you've heard about self-care. And I'm sure that every time you've heard about the importance of self-care you've thought, "Yes, I really need to do that more." So then why is it so hard to consistently make time for self-care when we so clearly recognize the value? I believe that the answer is a lack of self-love.

Very often we're trying to create a lifestyle that requires a level of self-love that we do not currently possess. And this will never work. Because the only thing that will fuel the sometimes challenging realignment of priorities that needs to be done, the boundaries that need to be protected and the uncomfortable feelings that need to be felt is a deep reservoir of self-love. You need to love and appreciate yourself so much that you only want to do things that will help you thrive, the same way you do for the people in your life that you love.

And how do we cultivate more love for ourselves? First, notice the Mean Voice and call it out as often as you possibly can. Give your Mean Voice a name and even a full visual description if you can. When it shows up and starts chirping at you and telling you all the ways that you're failing, all the things you'll never be able to do and all the things people are going to say and think about you, simply say, "Thanks so much Phil (or Susan or Darth Vader or whatever you've decided to name it) for trying to protect me, but I've got this. I've decided to make some changes around here. You're welcome to come along for the ride, but you're no longer allowed to drive the bus."

Then, with your Mean Voice sitting and watching from the back seat, you begin to take small steps towards showing yourself more love in the exact same way that you would show it for another person:

Communication - Eat mindfully, get quiet and listen to your body and what it's asking you for (beyond just the cookie cravings).

Trust - Trust that your body knows best and honour it when it tells you what it needs.

Integrity – If you make promises to yourself, keep them.

Respect – Respect your body enough to make it a priority.

Quality Time – Take time for the practices that help you be your best, such as planning and preparing healthy food, sleep, movement, meditation, and spiritual practice.

Generosity – Be of service to others (in a way that respects your own boundaries.

Fun - Make time for the things you absolutely love to do.

Gifts – Treat yourself and feel like you deserve it!

Honesty - Be honest about the excuses you're making, or the limiting beliefs you're allowing to stop you from making healthier choices.

Responsibility - Be the creator of your own life and your own experience. Don't blame carbs, time, or your family for the choices you make.

Compassion – Stop being so hard on yourself and stop talking to yourself in a way that you would never talk to a friend.

Do you see how the exact same elements that form the foundation of a healthy relationship with another person, are the ones that will begin to create a healthy relationship between you and yourself? And the only way that self-love starts to take hold and grow in your heart so that it can affect your thoughts, attitudes, beliefs and – ultimately – choices, is if you practice.

You don't just read this list and wake up tomorrow as someone who does all of these things and is bursting with self-love. Just like learning any new skill, you must commit yourself to practicing consistently and bit by bit you'll get better and better at it until it becomes automatic.

So, here is my challenge to you. Every day, maybe as part of your new morning routine, pick just one or two of these self-love elements and commit to implementing it wherever you can.

PILLAR FIVE: Fill Your Cup
TRY THIS

Make a plan ahead of time - Don't wait until you're exhausted or in the midst of a craving to try to make a healthy choice. Pick one habit that you'd like to change, anticipate what lies ahead and make a detailed and specific plan for exactly what you'll do that takes into account the trigger you'll encounter and the reward your brain will be looking for. Then simply practice executing your plan when the craving arises.

Make self-care your new priority - Self-care activities are those that foster connection with your truest, deepest self; with others who love you unconditionally; and with something greater than yourself. Look back at the list of self-care practices that I offered, pick a few that resonate with you and consider if you have any of your own that you'd like to add. Then take out your calendar and mark down exactly when you're going to make time for them. Schedule your self-care the way you'd schedule a dentist appointment or family commitment.

Consider the three areas of self-care you may not have thought of - Boundaries, the thoughts you think, and integrity. Where do you need to work on these in your life?

Daily tasks as self-care - Just by changing the way you perceive the tasks you do every day, many of them can actually become expressions of self-care. Choose one task that you currently do on an almost daily basis (i.e., washing the dishes, folding laundry, weeding your garden) and see if you can reframe your perception of it into an act of self-care.

Self-love - Consistent healthy choices must be fueled by a deep reservoir of self-love. You cultivate love for yourself in the same way you cultivate and nurture love for someone else: communication, trust, integrity, respect, quality time, generosity, fun, gifts, honesty, responsibility, compassion. Every day, maybe as part of your new morning routine, pick one or two of these self-love elements and commit to putting it into practice during your day.

CONCLUSION

If your bathtub is overflowing, it doesn't matter what number, size, shape or thickness of towels you have, they're never going to solve your problem until you first turn off the tap.

The same is true when it comes to our efforts to lose weight and stay on track with healthy living. If you don't first do the work to update the old operating system in your brain that's driving all of your behaviors, it doesn't matter what kind of diets, program, meal plans, recipes, shakes or bars you try, they're never going to solve the problem.

My goal with this book was to share with you the best of what I've learned about how you can go about updating that old operating system. When I initially sat down to write this book I thought to myself, based on everything I've learned and taught over the years and everything I've seen with my clients, students and through my own journey, if someone were to ask me, "What are the key steps I need to take to go from feeling stuck in old, unhealthy patterns with food to feeling free, in control and like the healthy choices were simply natural and automatic?" what would I tell them?

The answer to that question became the five pillars that we've just explored together. I knew that they would need to:

Get out of auto-pilot and start living in a more mindful way each day so that they could better understand their patterns and make more conscious and deliberate choices.

Know where they were going and get clear and specific about the vision they had for the future they were trying to create for themselves.

Feel the feelings, stop avoiding uncomfortable feelings like stress, boredom or even cravings and recognize that those feelings have messages for us and that food is an ineffective way to manage them.

Disrupt old programming by updating the old operating system that's constantly driving them back to their old, familiar patterns again and again.

Keep their cup full and get ahead of the problem by making self-care and loving themselves a non-negotiable priority.

But then, as I was editing the book, something dawned on me. While the five pillars did represent the elements that I believe someone would need to master in order to change their relationship with food, I realized that they're also the steps that we all need to take if we want to make *any* significant changes in *any* area of our lives.

Whether it's launching a new business venture, writing a book, going back to school or breaking any old habit, mastering these five pillars can form the foundation of any transformation you want to make for yourself.

They're not easy and your brain will fight you every step of the way as you work with them, but the more consistently you practice them, the more natural they will become and the more you'll be able to harness their power to help you create an entirely new relationship with food – and with yourself.

I warn you; this won't be a linear process. You're not going to go from point A to point B and end up neatly at point Z. Rather, it will be a dance. You'll take three steps forward and one step back, two steps sideways, and a giant leap ahead before spinning around and falling down. It's okay. Just get back up and keep on dancing. Be patient with yourself. It took you years to get here; it's going to take time to do this work of reprograming that old operating system.

Also, you don't have to do this alone. If you're on Facebook, come join the thousands of people in my community there called *Conquer the Food Fight.* It's an incredibly supportive group of people who are on the same journey you're on. We cheer each other on, keep each other accountable and share ideas and tools along the way. You can also visit my website at www.sarabest.com to drop me a line and let me know how you're doing.

Be brave; you can do this. You're stronger than you think and this is work that's worth doing.

FREE TOOLS

If you'd like a simple and free "Cheat Sheet" that I've created that compiles all of the tools, action items and exercises discussed in the book into one place, head over to www.sarabest.com/tap, send us your name and email address and we'll email you a printer-friendly copy right away.

You can also visit www.sarabest.com/free-tools to find a selection of other free downloads and videos on topics such as willpower, night-time snacking and mindful eating.

ACKNOWLEDGMENTS

Completing this book has truly been a dream come true for me. I'd like to thank my husband, Brad, my kids, Grace and Gavin and my mom and dad for always cheering me on, helping me find the space and time to write and making me believe that I could create something good.

I also want to thank every single one of my clients, students and members of my Change Your Brain – Change Your Body program. This book literally would not exist without you. You guys inspire me more than you'll ever know.

Made in the USA
Middletown, DE
25 January 2022

59618560R00120